PF

D0494911

SURFACE
MICROTOPOGRAPHY

Surface Microtopography

S. TOLANSKY, D.Sc., F.R.S.
Professor of Physics, London University

Interscience Publishers Inc. New York

INTERSCIENCE PUBLISHERS, INC.,
250 FIFTH AVENUE, NEW YORK I, N.Y.

Library of Congress Catalog Card Number 60–14000

MADE AND PRINTED IN GREAT BRITAIN

CONTENTS

v

PREFACE

THE aim of this book is to show what can be achieved by multiple-beam interferometry when it is applied to the study of the microtopographies of surfaces. This is essentially a personal record since it is exclusively devoted to an account of the work carried out in this field in my own laboratory during the past fifteen years. A considerable number of post-graduate students have worked under my immediate direction on problems posed by me and I have not hesitated to draw freely on the work reported in their degree theses, since I have consistently played an active and considerable part in the various investigations conducted. Thus it is that the bibliography at the end of this treatise gives reference only to my own papers and to the theses of my own students. All references to work by other authors (mainly historical) are included in appropriate places in the text itself. I am glad to acknowledge here the immense enthusiasm and industry of my young collaborators, for without their application this would have been much less comprehensive as a book.

A wide field of activity is covered, for I have always regarded interferometry as a challenge for the solution of very varied problems. Of the 359 Plates, only twenty-one have appeared in book form before. Although in one sense this treatise is an atlas in which the pictures are surface maps, playing the vital role, it is not a mere atlas, for the theory is described, the techniques are discussed, and the main results found are summarized. The contents are divided into eight separate sections, the chapters in each being grouped according to the possible concentration of interests of individual readers.

It would not be possible in one treatise to deal exhaustively with all our findings nor is it possible to include here more than quite a small fraction of the very large number of beautiful interferograms we have taken during the past fifteen years. However, our more important findings are discussed and summarized, largely with the view of showing what can be achieved with a good interferometric technique, despite the very real simplicity of the means used. This account is deliberately restricted to the observations made with multiple-beam interferometry, although we have developed and regularly use other optical techniques.

It must be emphasized that there has been real failure in some quarters to appreciate all the full power and elegance of a correct multiple-beam topographical technique. It is not sufficiently recognized that this offers us a most reliable, truly three-dimensional, microscopy and it suffices to mention that we can, and do, use magnifications up to 500,000 times (which are not empty) and have measured many crystal lattice spacings, one as small as 2·3 ångström units; and this is all with visible light waves plus really simple equipment.

It gives me pleasure to acknowledge permission from the Clarendon Press, Oxford, to use five pictures from my book *Multiple-Beam Interferometry* (1948) and from N.A.G. Press, London, to use sixteen pictures from my book, *The Microstructures of Diamond Surfaces* (1955).

S. T.

March 1959

PART ONE

THEORY OF MULTIPLE-BEAM INTERFEROMETRY
EXPERIMENTAL TECHNIQUES
SPECIAL REFINEMENTS

1. INTERFERENCE WITH MULTIPLE-BEAMS

Introduction—Topographical interference fringes—Interference with multiple-beams—Airy's formula—Reflection fringes—Multiple-beam interferometry—The phase condition—Linear displacement of beams—The effect of imperfect parallelism—Line-width of the source—The reflecting coatings—Dielectric multilayers—References.

Introduction

FOR some fifteen years I have been developing varieties of multiple-beam interference and applying them to the study of microtopography. During this period a wide range of surfaces has been studied and many reports have been issued (see bibliography at end). However, only a very small fraction of the thousands of interferograms taken have as yet appeared in print. It is one of my objects here to show what is in fact but still a very small selection from the available photographs, with the purpose of illustrating how powerful are these techniques. The aim is to show that multiple-beam interferometric methods can offer valuable information in a surprising variety of fields. It is fair to claim that these techniques have truly created a three-dimensional optical microscopy. Traditionally, microscopy showed objects effectively two-dimensionally and one could resolve, at best, detail as small as half a light wave ($\lambda/2$). Multiple-beam interferometry offers in addition a microtopographical contour map *in the up and down direction*, but it is possible, in extreme cases, to resolve 10 Å (i.e. $\lambda/500$ for green light).

This is not a technique which can be universally applied. For example, it has so far been of little value in the vast biological field of microscopy. Nevertheless, in physics, metrology, mineralogy, crystallography, metallurgy, metal physics, engineering, even in dentistry, and in numerous fields of chemical interest, multiple-beam interferometry can offer valuable information.

Thus the prime object of this text is to reveal the versatility of multiple-beam interferometry by examples selected from our researches. There is little point in overloading the content with specific numerical information. It is enough for instance to show that the sides of growth pyramids on quartz crystals are curved, without including the numerical data we have obtained about particular specific crystals. Such data

3

can be found in the individual research reports and student theses listed in the bibliography. Or again a qualitative illustration of the finish of a superfine grinding of a metal cylinder suffices, without bothering to quote root-mean-square values of roughness. The function of this report is to emphasize where and how the techniques have already yielded useful knowledge, in the hope that other workers will be induced to adopt them.

Some details of the principles and practice of multiple-beam interference methods have already been described in earlier books listed in the bibliography. It would therefore be unnecessarily repetitive to go into all details again here. Only sufficient theory will be summarized to permit of an appreciation of the practical techniques. Although multiple-beam methods were first tentatively exploited in some of my teaching courses in Manchester in 1938, the first published paper on the subject was in 1943 (Tolansky, *Nature*, **154**, 722, 1943). This was followed by topographical studies on mica, quartz and selenite. Fringes of equal chromatic order were first described in 1945 (Tolansky, *Phil. Mag.*, **36**, 225, 1945), and subsequently (Tolansky, *Proc. Phys. Soc.*, **58**, 654, 1946) the basic principles were laid down and these have guided the investigations, although much development in techniques has taken place since then. The later developments are all incorporated in this text and examples of results obtained with them are scheduled. Very little of the material discussed here has been published before, nor has such a critical comparison of the various techniques developed been made elsewhere.

Topographical Interference Fringes

Although Fizeau described his celebrated two-beam fringe system as far back as 1862 (*Compt. Rend.*, **54**, 1237, 1862), it was only twenty-one years later (*Journ. de Physique*, **2**, 411, 1883) that Laurent pointed out that in a two-beam interference system between a flat glass plate and another surface of complex shape (still nearly flat) the fringe pattern is effectively a contour map of the surface microtopography. From that time on, the use of interference fringes for the control and assessment of small departures from the plane became an accepted basic technique both in optical workshops and in many precision metal industries. An obvious extension was to treat Newton's rings as a measure of sphericity and thus test lens surfaces. The use of Fizeau fringes was first adapted to the study of the micro-surfaces of crystals by Siegbahn in 1932 (*M. Ak. Matem. Astro. Fysik*, **23**, 12, 1932), who placed an optical flat on the crystal and with a microscope secured two-beam Fizeau fringes in reflection. Cleavage steps and other micro-features were recorded but, despite the obvious value and extreme simplicity of the technique, it was hardly taken up, and suffered neglect. The use of two interfering beams has undoubtedly severe limitations compared with the multiple-beam methods used here, yet the Siegbahn method deserved much more extensive application than it earned for itself.

In technological workshops one arrangement adopted for using Fizeau fringes was that introduced by Laurent and is illustrated in Fig. 1.

A small pin-hole A is illuminated with monochromatic light. Almost invariably the green mercury line λ 5460 is used, for it is easy with a filter and a mercury vacuum arc to secure by this means a very bright mono-chromatic line-source of ideal colour for visual work, and also eminently suited to photography. For two-beam work the Wratten 77A didymium glass filter gives excellent monochromaticity. For multiple-beam work in addition a yellow filter can be adopted, which transmits a weakened green line and the two yellow lines λλ 5770, 5790. These three lines, if so filtered to be of more or less the same photographic intensity, prove to be a valuable combination for many transmission experiments in multiple-beam interferometry. It is not advisable to use more than one wave-length in two-beam *reflection* methods.

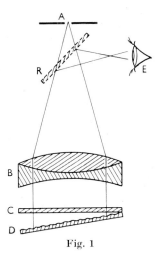

Fig. 1

In Fig. 1, B is a well-corrected lens and A is critically placed at the focus so that a parallel beam of light falls at normal incidence on to the optical flat C. Inclined to C at a small angle is the surface D under study. Interference fringes form between C and D and light is reflected back towards A. A half-silvered mirror R intercepts an adequate fraction of this and an image is formed at E either to be viewed by the eye or photographed.

Suppose C and D are plane surfaces, inclined to enclose a small air wedge, then in accordance with familiar principles a series of straight-line fringes is formed, the successive orders n, appearing at wedge thicknesses given by $n\lambda = 2\mu t \cos \theta$, in which λ is the wavelength, μ the refractive index of the medium and θ the angle of incidence (at these n values fringes are dark because of the π change in phase between the reflections at C and D, the one at a glass-air interface, the other at an air-glass interface). Here we have $\mu = 1$ and $\cos \theta = 1$ so that a series of equally spaced linear fringes appears, each neighbour corresponding to increase (or decrease) in t by $\lambda/2$. As to which is the increase and which the decrease can be assessed by several methods, the common practice being to press down, say the left-hand side of C whereupon the fringes will move in to the left if C is the thicker side of the wedge. If the contrary is the case the fringes will move to the right.

At normal incidence the fringes are localized effectively in the air film CD and can be viewed there by alternative methods, some of which will be discussed later.

Since each fringe is the locus of points for which t has a value to make n an integer these are called fringes of *equal thickness*. Clearly as each fringe indicates a region for which t is constant then essentially the fringes are contour lines of regions of equal air thickness. The contour lines represent each a height change of $\lambda/2$, i.e. 2730 Å for the green mercury line. If now one surface is plane and the other has some other conformation the fringes will exactly contour this other conformation and effectively give a contour map of the surface microtopography.

The simplest case to consider is that of the completely symmetrical case of a spherical surface matched against a flat surface ; i.e. the Newton's rings produced by a convex lens and a glass plate. The rings are nothing more than the contour-map lines for a spherical hill. Such contours in a geographical map are obtained by cutting the earth's surface features by a succession of equidistant parallel horizontal planes. In like manner Newton's rings can be considered as the contours resulting from cutting the lens spherical surface by parallel planes $\lambda/2$ apart.

In the sphere, being a symmetrical case, the contour pattern is unaffected by tilting the optical flat. For any general topography the same concept applies and the fringes are the intercepts of the surface by planes $\lambda/2$ apart which are, it is to be noticed, parallel to the matching flat. This last property can introduce obvious curious distinctions from the geographical case. Let us imagine a regular conical hill with axis vertical, standing on a flat surface, indeed a typical ' sugar loaf ' hill. There is available a variable, in that the matching flat can be tilted. If set parallel to the plane supporting the hill the situation produces what can be called the ' *geographical* ' dispersion, as in geographical contour maps. The fringes will now consist of a series of circles, since these are the intercepts between the matching plane and the cone. But now tilt the matching plane and the intercepts become the conic sections, i.e. ellipses. Thus it is that the particular fringe pattern given by the one and the same topography, a conical hill, depends upon the relative inclination of the matching flat. This makes no difference to interpretation although it is confusing to the beginner. The scale is distorted by the tilting, but the reinterpretation of the true microtopography from the fringe pattern is independent of the angle of inclination of the matching flat. Indeed it may be truly said that in practice rarely does one secure twice, independently, the same actual fringe pattern for any one topography, for the dispersion and the fringe orientation are matters of chance adjustments of the matching flat.

Again, the particular tilt of the reference plane, in inexpert hands, can lead to the overlooking of surface details. Imagine the surface to be a staircase in which the steps are broad, and let them be, for example, $\lambda/10$ in height. The matching flat could be set, so to speak, horizontal, then the fringes are straight lines in the directions parallel to the edges of the stairs. Fringe maxima only appear on every fifth stair, for only then has the height changed by $\lambda/2$. This is deceptive. If the flat is tilted so as to be higher on the left (or right) of the staircase the fringes now move diagonally across each step and so the step pattern is more adequately revealed. This indicates the necessity in general for taking at least two sets of fringe pictures with dispersions more or less in perpendicular directions.

The nature of two-beam fringes is such that the intensity distribution follows a $\cos^2$ law such that the light and dark parts are equal in width. Plate 1 ($\times$ 10) shows two-beam Newton's rings. It will be shown in following sections that *multiple-beam* interferometry is a technique which produces a very great sharpening of the fringe system and this leads to an altogether higher order of sensitivity and of accuracy in studying surface topography. An example of a multiple-beam pattern shown by a piece of glass is shown in Plate 3 ($\times$ 20). The different fringe character is obvious and the advantages are apparent apart from the general topography. The slight wriggles discernible in the fringes of Plate 3 are the micro-contour patterns of the surface polish irregularities. It will be recalled that fringe separation is 2730 Å and it will be demonstrated adequately later that fringe displacements as small as 1/250th of an order separation can be resolved and measured in ideal cases. This means that the very small height change of about 10 Å can be made visible. Indeed this is less than the molecular lattice spacings in many crystals. Herein lies the power of multiple-beam interferometry, but it is well to remember that this high resolution is in *the up-down direction only*. Thus the technique must be applied judiciously. It

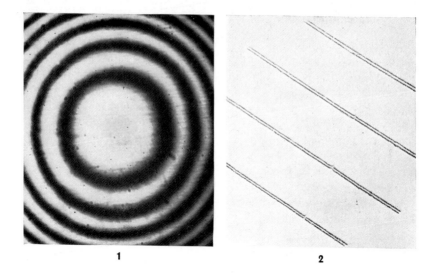

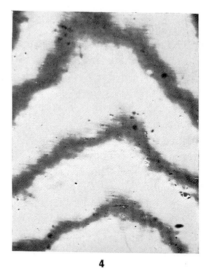

Plates 1-4

cannot be expected to reveal height changes of any details which are only ultra-microscopic in *extension*. In most instances one requires to have available a reasonable area of extension. A disc of say 1/100th mm diameter is often a limiting kind of size, although in special cases information is obtainable over a disc extending over little more than a micron. Generally speaking the area under observation should be appreciably greater than the limit of resolution of a 4-mm microscope objective. It can of course be macroscopic if suitable. Interferograms then produce contour patterns in which the height-depth size is greatly magnified, compared with the scale in extension. The ratio of scales can easily exceed 10,000 : 1 and this must be constantly borne in mind in interpreting interferograms.

Interference with Multiple-Beams

The history of multiple-beam interferometry shows a peculiarly slow development. By multiple-beams is meant the production of interference between two surfaces, employing a succession of coherent beams which are specifically related in phase and intensity. Ideally, the beams should be behind each other in phase, in an *arithmetical* progression, should fall off in intensity in a *geometrical* progression, and the series should be infinite. Such beams can combine and produce highly sharpened fringes. The theory of a multiple-beam interference effect between parallel plates was first given by G. Airy (*Math. Tracts.*, 1831, p. 381) who derived a general formula for the combination of a theoretically infinite number of beams between two surfaces, arising from successive multiple reflections to and fro between the faces of the plate.

This theory remained a forgotten academic curiosity until A. Boulouch (*Journ. de Physique*, **2**, 316, 1893) realized the significance of this formula and drew attention to the sharpening effect which results if the surfaces are coated with a high reflecting film. Then in 1897 Fabry and Perot (*Annales de Chimie et de Physique*, **12**, 459, 1897) developed their celebrated multiple-beam interferometer which consisted of two silvered, plane-parallel surfaces, and with this Fabry and others carried out for many years their striking fundamental classical series of measurements in metrology and spectroscopy.

The essential feature in this classical interferometer is that the surfaces, which are coated with silver, *are strictly parallel* and this permits development of the Airy condition. Fabry and Perot also applied the multiple-beam technique to thin wedges consisting of silvered planes enclosing a thin air wedge and indeed employed such wedges in some of their researches. They did not, however, make an analysis of the necessary conditions required to produce really sharp fringes, nor did they see the application of multiple-beam fringes to topography. The detailed analysis of the optical conditions necessary for high definition multiple-beam fringes from wedges had to wait until 1946.

It should be emphasized that the extension of the multiple-beam principle from plane-parallel surfaces to wedges is by no means a triviality. On the contrary it is a considerable development. For with plane-parallel surfaces the fringes, which are circular fringes of *equal inclination at infinity*, involve *integration* of light over the whole area of the planes. With wedges, the fringes are the *localized* fringes of equal thickness and these, on the contrary, give a highly localized topographical contour map, the fringes being critically localized on the surface under study when the light is incident normally.

In the following sections the development of the multiple-beam principle for plane parallel surfaces will first be reviewed and then its extension to wedges will be treated in detail.

Airy's Formula

Suppose, as in Fig. 2, we have two parallel plates separated by an air gap of thickness t, and let a light beam be incident at angle θ. For

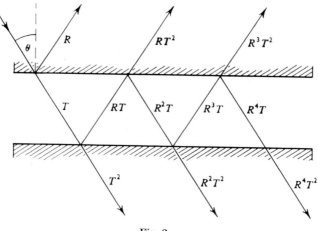

Fig. 2

simplicity (it does not affect the result) refraction can be disregarded and it is assumed that there is no absorption of light. A fraction of the light R will reflect at the first face and a fraction T will be transmitted. This will then meet the second where the amount RT will be reflected and T^2 transmitted. The whole operation will repeat itself and the net result is the *transmission* of a series of diminishing geometric intensity

$$T^2 + R^2 T^2 + R^4 T^2 \ldots, \text{ i.e. } T^2(1 + R^2 + R^4 + \ldots).$$

In like manner there is a *reflected series* $R + RT^2 + R^3 T^2 \ldots$, i.e. $R\{1 + T^2(1 + R^2 + R^4 \ldots)\}$. With the arrangement illustrated in Fig. 2 there is a difference in phase in reflection at the two faces. However, most multiple-beam interferometry requires the deposition of metallic mirrors on the faces, and with such mirrors the phase effect on coming to metal from air is not very different from that on coming to metal from glass. A further simplification is then possible by treating the phase on reflection as the same at both. Further, it will be imagined that the metal film is non-absorbing, but as this is not really true, account will be taken later of the modifications introduced by absorption.

Either the reflected light or the transmitted light can be collected by a lens and at the lens focus interference is produced. With an extended source (a range of values of θ) Haidinger's rings appear at the lens focus. It is not difficult to show that the rings, which are formed by the infinite multiple series of beams, occupy the same positions and obey the same law relating diameter to order of interference as the rings formed by two-beam interference. The effect of the multiple beams is to alter the *intensity distribution* within the fringe system and not the fringe position or diameter.

As is shown in elementary texts on optics, the sum of the infinite transmitted series leads to an intensity distribution within the fringe pattern given by

$$I = \frac{T^2}{(1-R)^2} \cdot \frac{1}{1 + \dfrac{4R}{(1-R)^2} \sin^2 \delta/2}$$

in which $\delta/2$ has the value $\dfrac{2\pi t \cos\theta}{\lambda}$. When $\sin^2 \delta/2 = 0$ (which happens at $2t \cos\theta = n\lambda$) I is a maximum and equals $\dfrac{T^2}{(1-R)^2}$. If there is no absorption then by definition $R + T = 1$ so that $\dfrac{T^2}{(1-R)^2}$ is unity. The fringe peak maximum, *without absorption*, has then the same intensity as that of the incident light.

The intensity has a minimum value [when $2t \cos\theta = (n + \frac{1}{2})\lambda$] which is equal to $\dfrac{(1-R)^2}{(1+R)^2}$. The fringe shape is independent of T and is determined only by the reflectivity R.

It was Boulouch who first recognized that a profound change in the shape of the fringe system arises when R has a high value, say 0·90. The result of such a high reflectivity is to change the fringe shape from the cos² intensity distribution of Fig. 3 into the multiple-beam intensity distribution of Fig. 4.

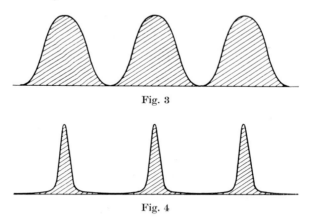

Fig. 3

Fig. 4

This was the important practical feature exploited so intensively by Fabry in his interferometric studies. Airy's formula for the fringe shape can be written (following Fabry) as

$$I = \frac{1}{1 + F \sin^2 \delta/2} \text{ in which } F = \frac{4R}{(1 - R)^2}$$

and has been called the coefficient of *finesse* (or fineness), since it determines the fringe shape. The width of a fringe is usually described by a

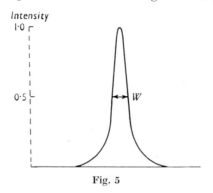

Fig. 5

quantity, the half-width W, which is defined as the width at half intensity, as in Fig. 5. A simple computation shows that the half-width occupies a fraction of the space between two orders equal to $\dfrac{0\cdot63}{F^{1/2}}$, which is near

enough $\dfrac{(1-R)}{3R^{1/2}}$. To a close enough approximation the values of the half-widths for reflectivities 0·7, 0·8, 0·9 and 0·95 are 1/8th, 1/13th, 1/27th and 1/58th of an order. With silver films as reflectors a reflectivity of 0·95 can be secured in the green region, and the fringe width is 1/58th of an order separation. It is clear from these width figures that high reflectivities are very important, an increase of a mere 5% from a reflectivity of 0·9 to 0·95 has more than doubled the sensitivity in that the fringe width is reduced to less than half by this slight increase. Under special conditions a reflectivity of 0·97 can be secured and this gives a fringe width of a mere 1/100th of an order.

The intensity of the minimum between fringes is $\left(\dfrac{1-R}{1+R}\right)^2$ and for the values of $R=0\cdot8$ and 0·9 and 0·95 these minima have intensities which are near enough 1/80th, 1/360th and 1/1520th that of the maxima. With the very high reflectivities, the regions between fringes can effectively be considered completely dark.

The derivation of the Airy formula requires integration of *all* the beams, and it is therefore implicit in these calculations that (*a*) the parallelism is perfect, and (*b*) the surfaces are truly plane. Neither condition can really be fulfilled in the Fabry-Perot interferometer, and fringe widths with this instrument often appreciably exceed those computed because of departures from these ideal conditions.

So far the influence of any absorption in the silver film has been disregarded. It can be seen that absorption merely influences the total intensity of the transmitted pattern *and not its shape*. The transmitted intensity is given by $\dfrac{T^2}{(1-R)^2}\dfrac{1}{1+F\sin^2 \delta/2}$ and in the event of there being absorption, the transmission T is now no longer equal to $1+R$. If A is the fraction absorbed at each silver film, $T+R+A=1$, whence $\left(\dfrac{T}{1-R}\right)^2$ becomes $K=\left(\dfrac{1}{1+\dfrac{A}{T}}\right)^2$. The coefficient of fineness F still remains independent of A, from which it follows that the whole pattern is reduced in intensity by the factor K. Now even with good silver films of reflectivity 0·95 it is quite difficult to secure a value of A less than 0·04. Taking this as a value obtainable with a good technique, K becomes 1/25th. Thus intensity is reduced to 1/25th of that of the incident light. Any attempt to push R beyond 0·95 leads to a catastrophic reduction in transmitted intensity since the transmission falls off very rapidly. Thus a mere increase in reflectivity by $\frac{1}{2}\%$ from 0·95 to only 0·955 (even without an increase in absorption, which in fact there would be) reduces the intensity to only 1/81th of the incident light.

In practice very careful attention must be paid to obtaining a low absorption. It is curious to remember that with zero absorption the transmitted peak intensity is always equal to that of the incident light, no matter what the reflecting coefficient might be.

Reflection Fringes

A reflection system accompanies the transmission system, yet apart from a single application which was made to spectroscopy (S. Tolansky and J. D. Ranade, *Physica*, **12**, 649, 1946), reflection multiple-beams do not seem to have been used in connection with the Fabry-Perot interferometer. The reason for this will become clear later. However, in surface microtopography the use of the reflected system is of much more general applicability than that of the transmitted system, for clearly reflected fringes can be obtained from an opaque body, such as a metal, by placing over this a suitable silvered optical flat. The successful development of a precision *reflection* system has made a most important contribution and, because of this, the applicability of the multiple-beam method for studying surface structure has been vastly extended.

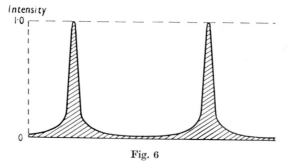

Fig. 6

It will be shown later that there are optical complications associated with the reflected system, but in the first instance a simplified approach will be made. This will disregard two characteristics, namely the effect of phase-change on reflection at the first surface and the effect of absorption. Neither can be neglected and both will be brought back into consideration later. It can readily be demonstrated that in this simpler treatment envisaged the reflection fringes are exactly complementary to the transmitted system. Fig. 6 and Fig. 7 show for comparison the predicted transmitted and reflected intensity fringe distributions. Fig. 7 is obtained merely by turning Fig. 6 upside down. Whilst the transmitted fringes are bright, narrow lines on a *dark* back-

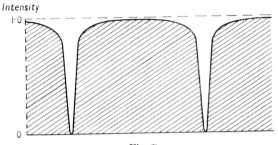

Fig. 7

ground, on the contrary the reflection fringes are dark, narrow lines on a *bright* background. The minima in Fig. 7 go down to zero, just as the maxima in Fig. 6 reach unity, and the maxima in Fig. 7 fall short of unity by the very small amount (1/360th for $R = 0.90$, for example) by which the minima in Fig. 6 are above the zero line.

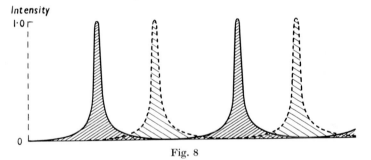

Fig. 8

The distribution in Fig. 7 leads to one marked difference between transmission and reflection systems. In transmission two or more separate wavelengths can be used as shown in Fig. 8, without either set affecting the other, but, in reflection, when two wavelengths are used the broad maxima of the one dilute the sharp minima of the other. Thus the contrast is seriously affected in that no fringes go down to zero (see Fig. 9). One can indeed secure fringes with, say, the two mercury yellow lines, but both sets suffer considerably in definition. There is then a major difference here, for it is really desirable to use only one wave length in reflection. This makes for increase in labour since, as will be shown later, order allocation often requires pictures to be taken with more than one wavelength. In transmission, a suitable filter enables, say, green + yellow lines to be utilized simultaneously, but, in reflection, separate pictures require to be taken. It is for this reason too that the Fabry-Perot interferometer when used for hyperfine structure studies has limited use in reflection.

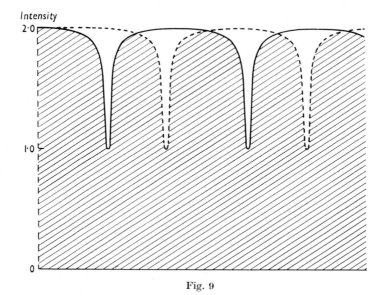

Fig. 9

On reference back to Fig. 2 it will be noticed that all the transmitted beams go *through* two films, so that each has a factor T^2 in its intensity term. This is true also for all reflected beams *other than the first beam*. Recapitulating, the transmitted series is $T^2(1 + R^2 + R^4 \ldots)$ and the reflected series can be written $R + RT^2(1 + R^2 + R^4 \ldots)$.

If the first term in the reflected series is cut out one is left with exactly the transmitted series (apart from being multiplied by a factor R). Since R is nearly unity, one arrives at the surprising conclusion that the cutting out of the first reflected term, which is much the most intense beam, converts the *reflected* system into a fringe pattern which is now identical with the *transmitted* system (it is merely a few per cent weakened because R is slightly less than 1). That this is the case was first demonstrated by O. Lummer (*Sitz. der Berl. Acad. d. Wiss.*, 1900, p. 504) and it is a property that can be exploited in special cases. When it is so exploited, the reflection fringes acquire effectively the properties of a transmitted system.

Now will be taken into consideration the first factor which was omitted in the simpler treatment, i.e. the absorption of the silver film. This has a profound and unexpected effect and it was only after the part played by absorption was realized (S. Tolansky, *Physica*, **12**, 648, 1948) that we succeeded in obtaining very high definition with reflection multiple-beam fringes for general topographical use.

Viewed simply, the effect of an absorption A is to reduce T to a lower value T_1 (i.e. from $(1 - R)$ to $(1 - R) - A$). In the series for reflection $R + [RT^2(1 + R^2 + R^4 + \ldots)]$ the quantity in square brackets is that which combines to bring the minimum down to zero. But now because of absorption the series has changed to

$$R + [RT_1^2(1 + R^2 + R^4 \ldots)]$$

and as T_1 is less than T the quantity in the square bracket is no longer sufficient to bring the fringe minimum to zero. Fringe appearance when absorption is slight is as in Fig. 10. When, however, absorption

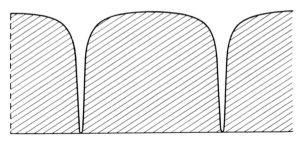

Fig. 10

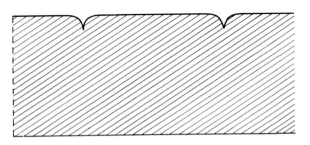

Fig. 11

increases, the pattern ultimately becomes like Fig. 11. The contrast is severely affected and the fringes can hardly be seen or photographed.

An alternative consideration which also gives a good physical picture of how absorption affects the fringes is as follows. It has already been demonstrated that the reflected system is built up of an amount R (nearly unity) combining with a series which is effectively the equivalent of the transmission series. Now it has already been shown how absorption greatly weakens the transmission series, so in like fashion one now has to combine for the reflection pattern the quantity R together with an effectively greatly weakened transmission series. So it becomes abundantly clear that whilst *fringe width* is determined by reflectivity the very important characteristic *fringe visibility* is decided by *absorption only*. If absorption is low the fringe contrast is high, the fringe minima dip very low and they appear dark against an intense bright background. If the absorption is high, the fringes will still be narrow but they will be hardly visible.

Hence, whilst high reflectivity is of course important, an essential basic condition in reflection interferometry is to have low absorption, otherwise fringes can hardly be seen. Indeed, in general, a slightly lower reflectivity for reflection than for transmission systems is advantageous. Correct silver film thickness is a highly critical matter in reflection interferometry and vacuum conditions must be impeccable to avoid absorption. *Failures to secure good fringes in reflection can often be attributed to an excessive absorption in the silver film.*

The second optical complication, that of irregular phase change, is best left for detailed discussion later, and it will suffice here if the nature of this effect is just indicated.

Reference again to Fig. 2 shows that there is another, so far disregarded, characteristic of the first very intense reflected beam. It is the *only beam*, among all those both reflected or transmitted, which lacks the factor T^2 and this is because it is the only beam which is not *transmitted* through two films. It is not transmitted at all. Apart from the intensity factor T^2, another optical quality is involved, namely the phase. All the other beams, having passed through two films, each identically acquire a certain phase change because of this. But the first beam is out of phase with all these by a slight amount because it has only been reflected and not twice transmitted. This can lead to some quite peculiar intensity effects which were first examined by Hamy (*J. Phys. Rad.* **5**, 789, 1906) and then studied in more detail in my laboratory by Holden in 1948. These intensity effects will be considered later.

Multiple-Beam Interferometry

What is now usually called ' multiple-beam interferometry ' was first developed by extending the multiple-beam principle from parallel plates to include wedges. Later other related systems were evolved and some of these will be discussed in due course. The detailed theory has been developed in *Multiple-Beam Interferometry* (Tolansky, Clarendon Press, Oxford, 1948).

In the formula $I = \dfrac{1}{1 + F \sin^2 \delta/2}$ the quantity $\delta/2$ which equals $\dfrac{2\pi t \cos \theta}{\lambda}$ is the only variable in a given interferometer. In the Fabry-Perot interferometer the condition which exists is that in which the flat plates are parallel, i.e., t is constant. Also, for any particular set of rings, λ is constant. The only variable is θ and this is why an extended range of angles is necessary, i.e. an extended source.

Now this Airy formula results because between strictly parallel plates the geometry is such that every beam which is reflected is retarded behind its neighbour by the same amount. Suppose we consider two flat plates not parallel, but inclined to include a small wedge angle, i.e. t is no longer constant but variable. If $\cos \theta$ is kept constant (preferably normal incidence so that $\cos \theta = 1$) and monochromatic light is used, then localized straight line wedge fringes appear.

If, despite the variation in t, a condition of a constant phase increase for successive beams can be maintained, then clearly from the Airy formula it follows that multiple-beam straight-line Fizeau fringes can also be produced having the same sharpened distribution as the circular Fabry-Perot fringes. Indeed they will be inherently sharper, for being localized there is not the integration over the total area with its associated deficiencies. It will be seen in what follows that the required phase condition can very closely be approximated to under special conditions, and when these are fulfilled, highly sharpened multiple-beam Fizeau fringes can be formed.

The Phase Condition

The way in which normally incident light produces localized multiple-beam fringes on the surface of an interferometer is illustrated in Fig. 12.

Let two silvered surfaces A and B be inclined at a small angle θ and such that a parallel beam of light 1 strikes A at normal incidence, and then meets B at X. Let the distance it travels between the plates be t. There will be another beam 2 which strikes A higher up, such that after two reflections it will, like beam 1, also pass through X. First, it deflects through 2θ at the plane B, and then through 4θ on plane A, finally to pass through X. Again still higher will be a beam 3, which deflects successively through 2θ, 4θ, 6θ, and 8θ, once more to meet X.

This goes on successively for n beams, the higher the order of the beam the further up must it begin. Beam intensities fall off in accordance with the same $T^2 R^{2n}$ rule met with in the case of the Fabry-Perot parallel-plate interferometer so that once again the higher the value of R the slower the fall off in intensity.

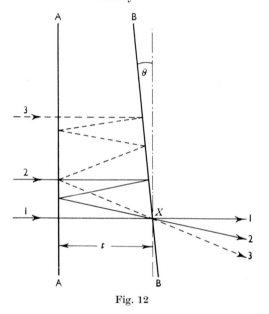

Fig. 12

It is immediately evident from the simple geometry that the successive beams do *not* follow behind each other in exact arithmetic progression. The path difference between beams 1 and 2 is not quite $2t$, it is to a first approximation $2t - 4t\theta^2$, i.e. there is a lag $4t\theta^2$. By extending this approximation to the nth beam I found that the lag for this nth beam is approximately $4\theta^2 tn^2$. Now Σn^2 from 1 to n is equal to $\dfrac{n}{6}(2n + 1)(n + 1)$ and if n is sufficiently large this is $\dfrac{n^3}{3}$. With a good reflectivity n in fact exceeds 60 so that closely enough this approximation is valid. Hence the path lag for the nth beam can be written as $\dfrac{4n^3\theta^2 t}{3}$. That my approximation is correct was confirmed later in my laboratory by J. Brossel (*Proc. Phys. Soc.*, **59**, 224, 1947) who used a more elegant analytical method, which gave in addition interesting results relating to the localization of fringes on planes other than the plane B in Fig. 12.

This computation of the retardation holds the key to the correct technique for multiple-beam interference, for clearly the Airy sum condition will be closely approximated to if, and only if, $\dfrac{4n^3\theta^2 t}{3}$ is less than $\lambda/2$. For it is evident that when this lag attains the value $\lambda/2$ for a beam, this particular beam *no longer assists* the Airy summation but indeed *opposes* it.

Thus an immediate aim must be to make $\dfrac{4n^3\theta^2 t}{3}$ as small as possible and certainly a good deal less than $\lambda/2$ for all the more important beams. It will be shown later that 60 beams (even 80) can frequently be used. For the sake of computation a maximum value of $n = 60$ will be adopted. Let it be assumed that for this 60th beam the maximum permissible retardation of $\lambda/2$ has been reached. It might appear at first that as variables both t and θ are at disposal for reducing the lag. But there are restrictions on the lowest value it is possible to adopt for θ. Calling the critical value of the separation t_c for which the lag is $\lambda/2$ then $\dfrac{4n^3\theta^2 t_c}{3} = \lambda/2$.

The value of θ, although a variable, cannot be reduced at will for Fizeau fringes. Its value depends on the magnification required to see the object contoured by fringes. It is essential to have at least two fringes in the field of view and often more are desirable. The higher the microscope magnification, the nearer to each other must be the fringes. If there are x fringes per centimetre on the surface then $\theta = \dfrac{\lambda x}{2}$ from which $t_c = \dfrac{3}{2n^3\lambda x^2}$. Taking $n = 60$ and $\lambda = 5 \cdot 46 \times 10^{-5}$ gives

$$t_c = \frac{1}{7 \cdot 9 x^2} \text{ cm.}$$

This gives an upper limit for t_c and, since the 60th beam should lag well behind $\lambda/2$, then t_c should certainly be below the value calculated. In round figures, it should be less than $\dfrac{1}{10 x^2}$ cm. When viewing objects at low powers, say $\times 10$, fringes can conveniently be 1 mm apart, i.e. $x = 10$ giving t_c as 1/100th mm, but for higher powers it is not unusual for fringes to be 1/10th mm apart, i.e. $x = 100$ (indeed fringe separation can often be very much less). But even at this dispersion of 1/10th mm the value of t_c is only 1/10,000th mm, which is about one-fifth of a light wave. Clearly, although the approximations are probably invalid by this time yet the general conclusion is inevitably forced on us namely : *the separation between the two surfaces must be very small, certainly of the order of a few light waves at most.*

This is the *key point* in the technique, and from this stem quite a number of other important optical consequences all of which can formidably affect definition.

It cannot be too strongly emphasized that the surfaces under examination should be brought effectively into contact. As will be amply demonstrated later, when a surface has elevations and depressions such that the elevations inevitably impose an increased t for the depressed regions, then the definition in these lower regions suffers considerably. Various devices have in some instances been successful for reducing t, but if this cannot be achieved then poor definition is inevitable and nothing can be done to restore the position.

Linear Displacement of Beams

A small value of t, quite apart from the decisive phase condition, plays another big role in maintaining good fringe definition and also in the physical meaning of fringe contouring. Referring back to Fig. 12 it is seen that the successive orders initially strike the surfaces A and B further and further away vertically from the region X. Sufficiently closely, for the nth beam, the distance away, d, from where the first beam strikes is $2n^2t\theta$. Using the former notation, as θ is $\lambda x/2$ then $d = n^2t\lambda x$. For $n = 60$ and $\lambda = 5{\cdot}46 \times 10^{-5}$ cm, to a rough approximation $d = \dfrac{tx}{5}$ cm, i.e. the displacement is proportional to t. It is evident that if t has the small values imposed by the phase condition, the value to which d is reduced becomes small. Take for example $x = 100$, i.e. fringes 1/10th mm apart then $d = 20t_c$. If the imposed value of t_c $(10^{-4}$ mm) is adopted then $d = 0{\cdot}002$ mm. The whole of the 60 beams thus come from a region comparable to the resolving power of a microscope. In effect the beams appear to come from one point and so there is identity between the object viewed and all the beams needed to produce the local fringe corresponding to that object.

When fringes are being produced between two plane surfaces the linear displacement only influences the fringe in so far as it is associated with the phase lag. But when a typically complex microtopography is under study then linear displacement plays a vital role. This is shown schematically in Fig. 13.

In this example the displaced beams are striking a variable topography and thus arbitrary path difference variations are introduced. Not only is the fringe broadened, but there is very little sense in its final interpretation.

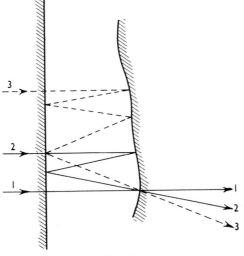

Fig. 13

The more violently complex the topography the more serious the effect. When high lateral magnifications (say $\times$ 1000) are used this defect is manifest. Often the topography imposes a local t value of at least a few light waves and it is then clear that higher order beams come from regions well outside the resolving power of the microscope. For this reason definition is usually considerably inferior in very high-power pictures unless plane regions are involved. Only in the special instances of very small t value can tolerably good definition be secured with simultaneous high lateral magnification in extension.

The Effect of Imperfect Parallelism

It has been assumed that incidence is normal and this can only be closely approximated to if a small source is placed at the focus of a well-corrected lens. The finite size of the source inevitably leads to imperfect parallelism in the incident light. The effect of an incidence other than normal is readily calculated. The order of interference obeys the rule

$n\lambda = 2t \cos \varphi$ where φ is the angle of incidence. For any value other than normal incidence $\cos \varphi$ is less than unity, from which it follow that for such values the fringe order corresponding to a given n displaces asymmetrically in the direction of increasing t. As Brossel indicated this can also be used for determining the up and down directions. At normal incidence $n = 2t/\lambda$ and at an incidence φ this changes to $n_1 = \dfrac{2t \cos \varphi}{\lambda}$.

If small angles are involved it is not difficult to show that approximately $n - n_1 = \dfrac{t}{\lambda} \cdot \varphi^2$. This quantity $n - n_1$ is the change in order produced by the deviation φ from parallelism.

On the average it is reasonable to assume that fringe width is about 1/40th of an order. It will be shown later that the best displacement measurable is about 1/5th of a fringe width, say 1/200th of an order. Adopting this as an extreme value above which the fringe should not be broadened, then the value φ which can be tolerated for 1/200th order is obtained directly by substituting $n - n_1 = \dfrac{1}{200}$.

The tolerance in φ for $t = 1/1000$th mm is 3°, for 1/100th mm it is 1°, and for 1/10th mm it is 1/3° of arc. If a 10-cm lens is used for producing the parallel beam, the sizes of the permissible apertures at the lens focus in these three cases are 6 mm, 2 mm, and 0·6 mm respectively.

This shows that the accuracy of the parallelism is directly dependent on the separation t between the surfaces. The smaller the separation the bigger the tolerance, i.e. the larger the tolerated aperture. When a microscope objective is used to illuminate a surface, a severe limitation is placed upon the size of the image at the back focal plane and a very small pin-hole source is then required to restrict deviations from parallelism. In such cases the importance of a small t value is overwhelming, especially with the higher-powered objectives.

Line-width of the Source

Another important advantage follows from the use of a small t value and this concerns the monochromaticity of the source used for the multiple-beam Fizeau fringes. Consider a Fabry-Perot interferometer of thickness t. The successive orders are separated by a wave-number interval $\Delta\nu = \dfrac{1}{2t}$. Making $t = 1/1000$th mm, gives $\Delta\nu = 5000$ cm^{-1}.

Ignoring for the moment the angular diameters of the fringes it is clear that an interferometer with so small a gap has a very low chromatic resolving power. It will be shown later that it is legitimate to treat a thin interferometer as a wavelength filter. Suppose it is assumed for convenience that there is a fringe at λ 5000 Å (wave-number 20,000 cm^{-1}), the neighbouring fringes will appear at wave-numbers 15,000 and 25,000 cm^{-1}, i.e. at wavelengths $\lambda\lambda$ 6666 Å and 4000 Å respectively. On the one side the fringe separation is 1666 Å, on the other 1000 Å. With the good practical fringe width 1/40th of an order this exceeds 25 Å of line-width. This is a most important conclusion, for it means that a natural line-width of as much as 5 Å can still be tolerated and yet only produce broadening amounting to the acceptable 1/5th of the width of a fringe ; 5 Å is a considerable line-width, indeed the widths of the lines from a vacuum mercury arc are usually well below this. Quite a hot, bright source can be tolerated with no fringe broadening, *provided t is small.* If t is increased to 1/100th mm then the relatively sharper line of width no greater than 0·5 Å is required.

It is invariably found in practice that fringe width increases rapidly with increase in t. This is due to the combination of all the factors just considered, each of which broadens the fringe. These broadening factors are then : (1) broadening due to increase in phase lag effect ; (2) confusion due to linear beam displacements ; (3) asymmetrical broadening due to deviation from parallelism of incident light ; (4) chromaticity effect of source line width.

The basic importance of reducing t to an absolute minimum is now clear. If the topographical conditions impose a t value greater than 1/1000th mm (and this they must if the fringe pattern exceeds a range of four fringes) then the fringe definition suffers in the region of the bigger t value.

This effect can often be seen when the wedge angle is fairly big. At the apex, where the two surfaces are close together, the fringes are sharp, but on moving progressively away from the wedge apex, as t increases, so also do the fringes progressively broaden. This is a defect that must be accepted in this type of fringe.

The Reflecting Coatings

Considerable experience indicates that only two types of coating are suitable for multiple-beam interferometry, namely (a) silver, and (b) dielectric multilayers, alternating zinc sulphide with magnesium fluoride (or, alternatively, cryolite). Silver films will be dealt with first. A suitable reflecting film requires three necessary characteristics. First it must have a high reflectivity, second the absorption should be low, and third the film must faithfully contour the surface. Silver films are best deposited by thermal evaporation in a vacuum of at least 10^{-5} mm Hg. Glass surfaces must be very carefully cleaned first with a detergent and a final cleansing with H_2O_2 solution is an excellent procedure. Only strongly resistant crystals like diamond, quartz, topaz, etc., should be cleaned with reagents. It is found that a final cleaning in the vacuum plant with a glow discharge is a wise precaution if good silver films are to be obtained. The details of evaporation technique have so often been described (see for example Tolansky, *Multiple-Beam Interferometry*, cited above) that it would be superfluous to go once more into detail. It is to be recognized that unless objects can safely survive a vacuum they cannot usually be silvered for multiple-beam interferometry.

In depositing a silver film, experience is required to learn the necessary film thickness, but once a reliable technique has been established a film can be reproduced by using standardized evaporating filaments with fixed amounts of silver on them, heating with standardized current in a given vacuum. The time of deposit (say 60 seconds) becomes then a sufficiently adequate measure of the character of the film. We do not go to the trouble of measuring the reflectivity and absorption, but employ an empirical test which is highly satisfactory and can be strongly recommended. This is as follows. When silver is deposited on a surface, alongside (on either side) are two pieces of glass, squares of side about 4 cm, which receive the same deposit. On removal, these two are held by hand, nearly parallel, and close to the eye. A bright source, such as a lamp filament, or better still a Pointolite, is viewed at a distance of about a metre through the pair of silvered plates. By imposing a slight angle between these, a train of successive images can be seen, falling off slowly in intensity. If R is the reflectivity and T the transmission, the intensity of the nth image is T^2R^{2n}. The sequence in this train of images is then a combined result of both transmission and reflectivity. Compare on this basis, three experimental films, A, B, C. Their reflectivities R, transmissions T, and absorptions A were measured as follows :—

$$\text{for A, } R = 0.95, \ T = 0.01, \ A = 0.04 \text{ ;}$$
$$\text{for B, } R = 0.90, \ T = 0.07, \ A = 0.03 \text{ ;}$$
$$\text{for C, } R = 0.85, \ T = 0.13, \ A = 0.02.$$

These are typical observable data for silver films.

It is found in practice with a good film like A, that one can see as many as 60 images. The intensity of the 60th image in this case is only 2×10^{-7} that of the incident light, but it will be provisionally assumed to be a threshold which can be observed from a Pointolite source. The image intensities depend in a critical manner upon both

T and R. Calculation shows that for the second film, B, the same intensity (2×10^{-7}) is reached at the 46th image, whilst for the third film, C, it is already attained at only the 34th image. Clearly the image counts, respectively of 60, 46 and 34, are a most sensitive empiric assessment, especially for the higher reflectivity.

Our empiric rule is to accept films that give 60 images or more. Occasionally as many as 80 images can be counted, with particularly good films. I have indeed on a few rare occasions even reached as far as 100 images. It is usually not even necessary to make a count, for the slow rate of falling off in intensity and in the colour of the higher order images enable a rapid assessment to be made, often merely at a glance. The image colour changes to a deep yellow and perhaps red, because reflectivity is higher for the red end of the spectrum than for the blue end. Experience shows that the slower the approach to a deep yellow colour the better the film, for the wavelength–reflectivity curve is flatter for the better film, so that the blue light persists longer for a good than for a poor film.

It will be adequately proved later that films deposited in a vacuum have remarkably accurate contouring properties. They do in fact contour micro-structure down to molecular dimensions. The film thicknesses used are of the order of 500 to 700 Å. Films thicker than 700 Å have too small a transmission, indeed a 1000 Å film is effectively opaque.

Dielectric Multilayers

When dealing with opaque surfaces and using reflection fringes, advantages are to be gained by coating the matching flat with a dielectric multilayer. It will be shown later that the *object itself* under study *should only be coated with silver* and *not* with multilayer, the multilayer being restricted to the matching flat alone. The great attraction of the multilayer is the fact that it has *very low* absorption and thus gives very high contrast in reflection fringes. The multilayer technique has been adequately described elsewhere (see bibliography) and here only the properties essential to interferometry will be reviewed.

If a thin film of thickness $\lambda/4$, of a dielectric material of refractive index greater than that of glass is deposited on to glass, then the reflectivity of that glass is enhanced. A suitable material which can be deposited with controlled thickness in a vacuum is zinc sulphide, with refractive index 2·37 (for sodium light). Because the retardation at normal incidence of the light from the two faces is $\lambda/2$, and as a $\lambda/2$ path due to phase change occurs (as the lowest face is in contact with a lower refractive index) the beams reflected from top and bottom of the film interferometrically unite and reinforce, with the result that because of the high reflectivity at each interface, due to the high refractive index, the combined effect from the double interface makes the reflectivity of the coated glass face jump from the usual 0·04 to no less than 0·31.

This mechanism of enhanced reflectivity can be repeated by putting down on top of this zinc-sulphide film first a *low* index film of thickness $\lambda/4$ (cryolite has a refractive index 1·36 and is admirable for the purpose), and then again on top of this another *high* index zinc-sulphide $\lambda/4$ film. The triple combination now has reflectivity 0·67. The procedure can again be repeated and it is found that five layers give reflectivity 0·87, seven layers give reflectivity 0·94, and nine layers give the very high reflectivity 0·97.

Apart from these reflectivity figures, there is another and, for our purpose, more important characteristic. Zinc sulphide and cryolite (sodium aluminium fluoride) are colourless transparent crystals and in thin films of thickness a mere $\lambda/4$ their absorptions are extremely low indeed. In practice some slight thermal dissociation of the materials appears to take place during evaporation and this leads to an increase in absorption. Yet it seems well established that none of these various multilayers (when correctly made) has absorption greater than 0·01 for the whole complex.

Comparing a seven-multilayer film with the corresponding silver film (which has about the same reflectivity of 0·94), in the case of silver the experimental absorption might be 0·04, whereas in the multilayer it is usually $< 0·01$ and this, as already pointed out, makes a tremendous difference to the contrast in reflection interferometry. We have therefore often used such multilayers. They are ideal for Fizeau fringe work, *provided that the technique of manufacture is good enough to ensure that the high reflectivity is in a region near to the green mercury line.* For it is clear by the very nature of a multilayer that the successive films can only be $\lambda/4$ thick (optically, not metrically) *for one specific wavelength.* As a result of this, a good multilayer has sharp chromaticity. It has its high reflectivity limited to quite a narrow wavelength band and the reflectivity falls off rapidly on either side of this wavelength maximum peak.

In practice quite a refined technique is needed to localize the maximum close to the desired wavelength λ 5460, and often a multilayer will be made which has, it is true, quite high reflectivity at the peak, but the peak is not at the correct wavelength. A rapid test for localizing the wavelength of the reflectivity maximum has been devised and this

will be described later when another fringe system is under consideration. If this precaution is not taken the most deplorable results can be
obtained with the green mercury source. For although the multilayer
can have quite a high reflectivity it may exhibit a very low reflectivity
in the region of λ 5460, giving hopelessly bad fringes with this light,
far worse indeed than a mediocre or even a very poor silver film. This
happened often until the introduction of the test, to be described later.

REFERENCES

Nos. 2, 3, 5, 10, 14, 16, 22, 33, 40.

2. INSTRUMENTATION

Transmission fringes—The quality of multiple-beam Fizeau fringes—Evaluation of fringe displacement—The first reflected-beam phase defect—The aperture of the collecting lens—Reference.

Transmission Fringes

THE simplest arrangement that can be used for low magnification up to say × 10 is shown in Fig. 14. A is a light source, a mercury vacuum arc, B a green mercury filter, preferably Wratten 77A. This can be replaced by a selected yellow filter which passes both yellow and green lines in about equal amounts. The condenser lens C throws an image of A on to the good iris diaphragm D, which can be reduced to quite a small aperture. D is at the focus of E and a parallel beam, at normal

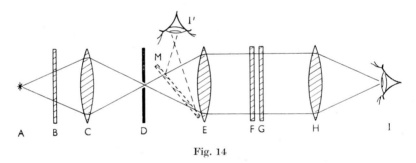

Fig. 14

incidence, falls on the interferometer F–G. Correct collimation is judged by superposing the back-reflected image of D on itself. The lens H brings the light to the eye I, where fringes can be seen. Alternatively H can be replaced by a camera. Essentially the same arrangement is used for high powers, but now H–I is replaced by a microscope, and as usual either the eye, or an eye-piece camera can then be employed. Much work is done with a microscope and a suitable arrangement is that shown in Fig. 15.

The iris is now at A and the collimating lens at B. A plane mirror C turns the light vertical. The condenser is removed since the incident light must be parallel and the interferometer D is placed on the microscope stage. The interferometer system uses a simple jig. The object under study is fastened with Gelva cement on to a glass disc before coating with silver. Gelva is unaffected by the vacuum and has itself no effect on the silvering. The matching flat is also a glass disc of the same diameter as that holding the specimen. With three screws, separated with weak helical springs, the two surfaces can be brought very close together and the position of the wedge apex can be adjusted at convenience to arrange a suitable fringe dispersion. The fringes are

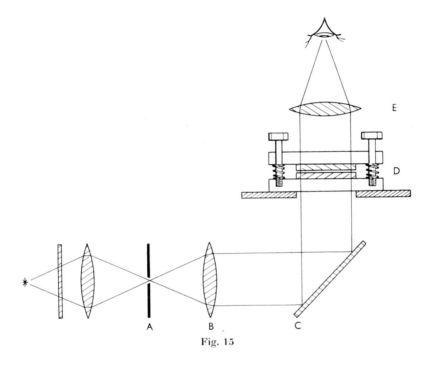

Fig. 15

then viewed with the microscope objective E which is focused on the space between the interferometer plates. In the sketch the eyepiece is left out.

The available distance ED depends on the working distance of the objective lens E.

For lenses of no greater power than a 16-mm objective the glass ' flat ' can be made from selected thin glass sheet, as will be shown later. Powers up to a 3-mm dry objective can be used, but in such cases the matching ' flats ' must be sufficiently thin (microscope cover slips) to permit of focus on the interference film.

For simple low-power reflection fringes, it is only necessary as in Fig. 14 to introduce a half-silvered mirror (indeed a piece of glass suffices) at **M**, when the reflected fringe system appears at **I′**.

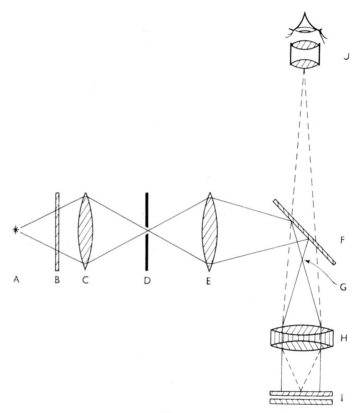

Fig. 16

In the more general case of reflected fringes, when using a microscope, a new optical difficulty arises. For powers above that of a 25-mm lens, the small lens working distances prevent introduction of a reflector between microscope and object. It becomes necessary to use a metallurgical type of microscope with surface illuminator. An arrangement is shown in Fig. 16.

Here **A** is the source, **B** the filter, **C** a condenser which images the source on **D**. Now contrary to the transmission case, **D** is not at the focus of the lens E, for instead of using incident parallel light, E is situated to throw at G a small image of the aperture D (by means of the glass reflector F). The image G must be critically at the back focus of the lens H. By this means the object I is illuminated by parallel light at normal incidence. However, the distance HI must be at the correct microscope setting to give an image of I in the eye-piece at J. The objective H has then two functions : (a) to produce a parallel beam from the back focal plane, and (b) to give a good image from I. A good combination of these two optical properties is by no means a characteristic of every make of lens. We have found different designs of lenses by different makers vary considerably in this respect, but have by now built up a collection of lenses which all adequately satisfy the two conditions. *For higher powers the size and position of D are very critical.*

The Quality of Multiple-Beam Fizeau Fringes

We have now reached a point in our discussion where all the foregoing considerations can be applied to the production of multiple-beam fringes, and here we will examine some examples. One minor item of theory remains yet to be discussed, that of the effect of the out-of-phase character of the first reflected beam, but the discussion of this will be held over as yet, since it has an effect not normally noticed when sufficiently high reflectivities are used.

In transmission pictures the fringes appear as bright lines on a dark background and in reflection as dark lines on a bright background. For reproduction in book-printing a narrow black line prints more reliably than a narrow white line sandwiched between two broad dark areas. It is thus often advantageous to turn a print back into a negative, into what in fact is actually obtained on the plate in practice. We shall often use such negative prints in the illustrations here. Such a procedure is only necessary with transmission fringes.

There are available in my laboratory two costly optical flats of exceptional quality, correct to $\lambda/80$ over 7 cm diameter, made in 1935 by A. Hilger. An interferogram ($\times$ 10) over part of these, using the two yellow mercury lines as source, is shown in Plate 2. Attention can be drawn to numerous characteristics. The fringes are almost exactly parallel straight lines. They are separated at one end by 18 mm and at the other end by 17·7 mm. They appear in pairs (λ 5770, λ 5790) but order separation is the interval between pairs. The separation of the doublets increases slightly from 0·7 mm at the one side to about 0·8 mm at the other. They are nearer at the wedge position where t is smaller. The doublet separation is then about 1/20th order, perhaps less. The fringe width itself is about 1/3rd of the doublet separation, i.e. something like 1/60th of an order which is only some 45 Å. Fringe definition is superb and all the small irregularities, some of which displace appreciably less than a fringe width, represent polish marks. A ' deep ' scratch about 1/20th of an order deep, say about 130 Å, is clearly visible running across the surface. The high sensitivity of the fringe system is very evident.

Now a comparison will be made between a multiple-beam and a two-beam interferogram of one and the same surface having on it a more complex topography. Plate 3 (× 20) shows the multiple-beam interferogram of a rough piece of glass, whilst Plate 4 (× 20) shows the two-beam picture of nearly the same region. The difference is notable. The multiple-beam fringes are extremely fine and reveal a complete secondary microstructure entirely lost in the broad two-beam fringes.

The magnifications on these pictures are to be noted. Fringes in both Plates 2 and 3 are some 2·0 cm apart, but they represent height changes of (roughly) $2·5 \times 10^{-5}$ cm. Magnification in depth is then × 80,000 and this is not, by any means, empty magnification, for the fringes are so fine that indeed displacements of one-fifth of a fringe width are measurable, i.e. about 1/250th order. *This approximates to 10 Å.*

When the technique is correct the contouring of micro-detail is most faithful. Plate 5 (× 50) shows an interferogram of the surface of a diamond which had been polished after sawing. Polish is incomplete and there are residual striated machine saw-cut markings, which the fringe pattern contours and shows with beautiful clarity. All the fine detail is contoured. In such an interferogram the dispersion can be varied by altering the angle between the surfaces. In Plate 6 (× 50) the same surface is shown but with the dispersion increased by a factor of 3 such that there is now only one fringe in the field of view. The magnification is now × 200,000. Yet fringe definition is still very good and much fine detail is observable.

At this point attention is drawn to some statements which have at times been *injudiciously made by others*, that multiple-beam interferograms are blurred and do not accurately contour fine detail. Such statements are only too clear evidence of the possession by the maker of the statement *of a very inadequate technique*. It is easy enough to secure poor, broadened, multiple-beam fringes, but *it is only with careful attention to all detail that one can hope to obtain such high definition pictures as those in Plates 5 and 6*. The higher the magnification used the more difficult is the situation, but numerous examples will be given later in

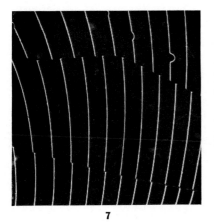

5

6

7

8

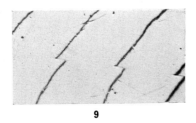

9

Plates 5-9

the text wherein the close contouring of micro-detail is well established.

If the surface exhibits discontinuities as shown, for instance, in the transmission picture Plate 7 (× 50) which is the interferogram of part of a mica cleavage, then several wavelengths must be used to allocate orders.   Plate 8 (× 20) is such an example from a mica face, which has discontinuities on it, allocated by using three wavelengths.   Three wavelengths are present to enable one to allocate orders.   In the monochromatic picture of Plate 7 neither (a) the direction of the discontinuity, nor (b) whether it is more than one order, are known.   It is easy to be tricked and a check must always be made.

Evaluation of Fringe Displacement

Consider a small cleavage step on mica as in Plate 9 (× 75).   Then the step height is $dn.\lambda/2$ in which dn is the fraction of an order of the displaced fringes.   Now the evaluation of dn with Fizeau fringes can at times introduce difficulties (these are overcome in other fringe systems to be discussed later).

If fringes on each side of the dividing line are equidistant as in Fig. 17 then clearly dn is $\dfrac{BB'}{AB}$.

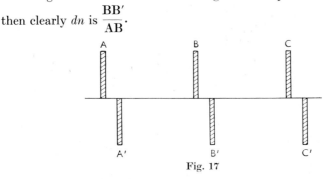

Fig. 17

However, the very structure of the surface studied affects separation between the fringes, as is seen for example in Plate 8.   If there is a *regular* change in dispersion then no serious error is introduced by taking

$$dn = \frac{2BB'}{A'B' + BC}.$$

This is effectively averaging the dispersion on either side of the step. If there happens to be either a rapid change of dispersion, such as occurs near the top of a hill or the bottom of a valley, or if a local defect disturbs the pattern, then other methods must be used.

In measuring a step, an ideal situation is created for measuring the displacement in that the fringes are above and below a separating line.

The eye is very sensitive to discontinuities of the kind shown in Fig. 18 and it is found possible to detect and measure a displacement which is only a fifth of a fringe width because of the advantageous fiduciary matching system.

Not all topographical features involve discontinuities. Curvature and sharp angles (on crystals) are
very frequent. Measurement of such face angles is
easily carried out interferometrically, for the surface
drops (or rises) $\lambda/2$ per fringe so that surface angles
can be estimated often at a glance.

Before going on to consider a further valuable
type of fringe system, two optical effects in Fizeau
fringes will be considered. The discussion has been
left till now because in practice these defects are
easily overcome and need not be present with a
correct technique. The first effect to be considered
is that due to the first reflected beam being out of

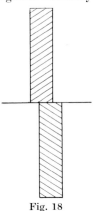

Fig. 18

phase with the rest of the reflected beams, an influence which can affect reflection fringes.

The First Reflected-Beam Phase Defect

The influence of the first beam phase defect was first noticed by us experimentally and then later fully explained in detail by Holden (*Proc. Phys. Soc.*, **62**, 405, 1949). The effects observed with low reflec-tivities are quite complex, but fortunately these all virtually disappear

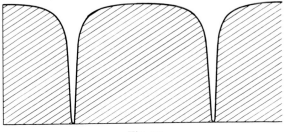

Fig. 19

when the reflectivity is high. When a correct calculation is made, taking into account the phase dependence of the first beam on film thickness, the end result is to show that reflection fringes are not symmetrical. They acquire what can be described as a ' saw-tooth ' shape. Instead of the theoretical shape shown in Fig. 19 which is produced when phase defect is neglected, the real shape becomes that of Fig. 20. This can be thought of in the sense that the dark reflected fringe has a bright neighbour peak alongside, bright since the peak is *above* the level of the general background. The effect is accentuated if focus is not correct. A typical example of this defect is shown in Plate 10 (× 60) which was taken on the surface of a topaz cleavage. The silvering on the flat was deliberately too thin and the wedge angle fairly high.   Holden has

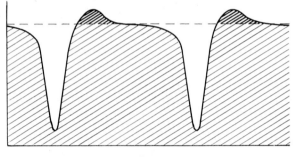

Fig. 20

shown that both of these conditions contribute to increase the defect. It is quite clearly seen how each dark fringe has a bright neighbour peak alongside.

A much more violent example is shown in Plate 11 (× 300) which illustrates fringes on an aluminium crystal. This interferogram has been deliberately arranged to emphasize the defect by having far too low a reflectivity and a high wedge angle.

The defect becomes progressively less and less marked with increase in reflectivity and has virtually disappeared by about reflectivity 0·80. It is quite non-existent at the reflectivities normally advocated for interferometry and does not appear on the numerous good quality pictures shown later.

A second defect will now be considered. This is much more likely to occur if the optical arrangement is incorrect.

The Aperture of the Collecting Lens

Even when the incident light is parallel and also incident normally, when such light falls on a wedge it is apparent that the ultimate emerging beams diverge. The higher the beam order, the more the divergence. If the two interferometer surfaces are inclined at an angle θ then the nth beam emerges, diverging at an angle $\Psi = 2n\theta$ since it has suffered n deflections each of 2θ. If there are x fringes per centi-

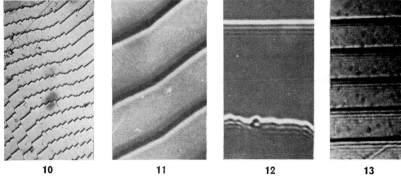

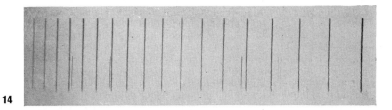

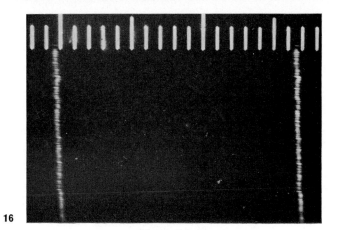

Plates 10-16

metre on the wedge then $\theta = \dfrac{\lambda x}{2}$ so that the divergence Ψ equals $n\lambda x$

radians. Taking the 60th beam, which is what we are agreeing to consider as the last beam of effective intensity, then for the green mercury line, this 60th beam diverges through the angle $\Psi = 0\cdot18x°$.

With a microscope, the fringes are often even less than 0·1 mm apart, i.e. $x = 100$ so that the divergence of the 60th beam is, in such a case, actually as much as 18°. That the divergence is large is easily demonstrated in the case of microscopic observation by removing the eyepiece and the beams can then be seen traversing the objective lens.

The beams do not displace symmetrically, but only in the one way imposed by the direction of the wedge apex. The collecting angle of the lens should thus be twice the 18° of the diverging beam and this requires a numerical aperture of some 0·3.

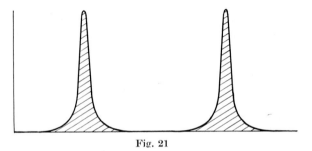

Fig. 21

If a smaller aperture is used then there is incomplete collection of beams. This has two effects : (a) the fringes are broadened appreciably, and (b) the fringes are accompanied by ghosts.

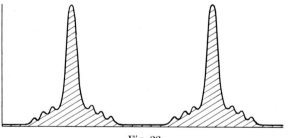

Fig. 22

The theory of the fringe pattern produced by a multiple-beam series which is cut-off instead of going to infinity was given long ago by E. Gehrcke (*Anwendung der Interferenzen*, Vieweg Braunschweig, 1906).

It is the case which occurs in the Lummer-Gehrcke interferometer and it has been well established that the result is to change the distribution from the continuous form in Fig. 21, which is that for an infinite series, to the form shown schematically in Fig. 22, which shows secondary ghost maxima. The less the number of beams combining the more intense are the secondary maxima, and the broader are the main fringes.

This effect appears in practice occasionally, but only if the collecting lens has an insufficient aperture. The effect is not usually very marked and since wedges are involved it is seen as asymmetry in which faint ghost fringes appear on one side of the main fringe. Plate 12 (× 150) is a typical example of this effect on transmission fringes. If it occurs it need not seriously influence the interpretation or accuracy in carrying out the microtopographic analysis.

The ghost image effect can be shown up well in reflection fringes if the aperture is cut down and the reflectivity is reduced. Plate 13 (× 50) shows the complex pattern obtained in such an instance, ghost images, and adjacent bright image seen best in the upper fringes, confusing the whole situation. Such anomalies are, of course, always avoided in practice, but are mentioned here as a warning.

REFERENCE

No. 22.

3. FRINGES OF EQUAL CHROMATIC ORDER

Evaluation of the fringes—Uses of fringes of equal chromatic order —Birefringence—The optical flats—The testing of multilayers— References.

A DESCRIPTION will now be given of a multiple-beam fringe system first described in 1945 (S. Tolansky, *Phil. Mag.*, **36**, 225, 1945) and which has proved to be of considerable value in the study of microtopography. The way in which this system arises can be understood from a consideration of the properties of the Airy intensity formula written in the form $I = \dfrac{I \max}{1 + F \sin^2 \delta/2}$. In the general case of silvered plane-parallel plates, separated by t and a medium of refractive index μ, with light incident at φ and of wavelength λ, then δ has the value $\dfrac{2\pi}{\lambda} . 2\mu t \cos \varphi$.

In this there are at disposal four quantities, t, λ, μ, φ. For air films μ can be taken as equal to 1 and this reduces the variables to three, t, λ, φ. The Fabry-Perot interferometer is that in which t is constant (plane-parallel plate) and φ is then the variable, for λ is constant for a monochromatic line.

Multiple-beam wedge fringes of the kind already discussed arise when both λ and φ are constant (usually $\varphi = 0$) and t is the variable.

Now consider the types of fringes that can be obtained with *white light*, which means that λ is now variable.

Fringe systems only become visible if the complex of superposed white light fringes is dispersed with a spectrograph in a manner to be discussed later. There are two possibilities, one of which is of interest to spectroscopy and the other to topography. The spectroscopic system was described first by E. Gehrcke and O. Reichenheim (*Ver. D. Phys. Ges.*, **4**, 209, 1906). It arises if a Fabry-Perot interferometer is placed before a spectroscope, illuminated with white light and then the mixed fringes (which are at infinity) are brought to a focus on the slit of a spectrograph. Because t is fixed and λ and φ vary, a set of close-packed *curved* fringes is seen in the spectrograph. With the usual spacings of a Fabry-Perot interferometer these are so finely packed that it requires usually a high-power spectrograph to resolve them. They have found occasional use in spectroscopy. If the value of φ is restricted to normal incidence then one obtains the channelled fringes described by E. Edser and R. Butler (*Phil. Mag.*, **46**, 207, 1898). With good silverings such fringes are sharp and the system can essentially be regarded as a *wavelength filter*, passing a series of discrete wavelengths. If t is the distance between the plates, the separation of the straight parallel Edser-Butler fringes is given, in wave numbers, by $\Delta \nu = \dfrac{1}{2t}$. It is for this reason that, say, with a 1 cm Fabry-Perot interferometer both Edser-Butler and Gehrcke-Reichenheim fringes are so closely spaced (i.e. 0·5 cm^{-1}). Attention is drawn to the fact that the position of the Edser-Butler fringes is quite independent of the position of the interferometer as long as normal parallel light falls on the system, and on the slit. This is not the case with the white-light fringes of Gehrcke and Reichenheim which require critical focus on the slit of the spectrograph.

Now consider what takes place if white light is used (λ variable), φ is kept constant (normal incidence preferably) and t varies also, i.e. a wedge. It now becomes essential *to throw an image of the wedge on the slit of the spectrograph*, using the arrangement shown in Fig. 23.

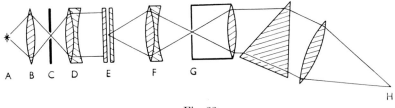

Fig. 23

A is a carbon arc and with the lens B an image is thrown on to an iris diaphragm C. This is at the focus of a good achromat lens D which throws a parallel beam on the silvered interferometer E. F is either a good achromat or else an achromatic microscope objective, and with it an image of E is projected critically on the slit C. The slit is narrow and the fringes in question are photographed at H.

In spite of an incident parallel beam on E, the emerging beams will diverge, as usual because of the wedge effect. Now as t and λ both vary, it is evident that the fringe order n is given by $\dfrac{2t}{\lambda}$. A fringe is essentially the locus of points for which n has one value. An image of the wedge is thrown on the slit and therefore different positions on the wedge correspond to different values of t. Each point (each t value) will act as a wavelength filter, with fringe spacing $\Delta\nu = \dfrac{1}{2t}$. Integrating along the slit will clearly lead to fringes in which t/λ is constant, as this is chromatic, the name fringes of equal chromatic order has been adopted.

If the two surfaces are parallel, then the fringes are straight lines. Plate 14 ($\times 2$) shows a typical set of such fringes extending over part of the visible spectrum (a line spectrum is superposed). Because of the variable dispersion of the prism spectograph the fringes are nearer together at the red end (left). What is noticeable is that, despite the use of white light, the characteristic sharpness due to the Airy summation is apparent.

Now these fringes offer considerable optical advantages. Consider first Plate 15 ($\times 10$). These are given when the interferometer E is a silvered Newton's rings lens-plate combination. The following should be noticed:

(1) Each fringe is identically the same as its neighbour, due allowance being made for the variation of spectroscopic dispersion (with a grating spectrograph they are of identical shape).

(2) Each fringe is in effect a profile of the section of the surface selected by the spectroscope slit.

(3) The spacing of the fringes is determined only by the separation t of the two surfaces of the interferometer. If these are close together very high dispersion and enormous magnification is possible.

(4) The spacing of the fringes does not depend on the angle between the surfaces. This is most important, for it is possible to use a high-power microscope in place of the lens F *without* increasing the wedge angle ; indeed, the surfaces can be made as closely parallel as possible (this should always be aimed at). Thus in our phase lag retardation formulae (lag $\dfrac{4n^3\theta^2t}{3}$) and for beam displacement ($2n^2t\theta$), θ can be reduced until only the small residual value produced by the topography itself is operative. Thus it is that inherently the fringes of equal chromatic order can be made sharper than Fizeau fringes.

(5) The directions of the curvatures of the fringes shows at once whether one is observing a hill or a valley. (This is a matter of difficulty with Fizeau fringes.) A moment's consideration indicates that a hill bows the fringes convex to the violet and a valley bows them concave to the violet. Thus direction of elevation or depression can be settled at a glance.

(6) The fine structure in the fringes reveals the polish marks on the glass. Here we have a powerful method for studying very fine micro-

structures. Consider for example two of the fringes of equal chromatic order given by a pair of polished optical flats, shown in Plate 16 ($\times$ 50). This refers to a 1-mm length of the flats. The micro-polish marks are very clearly seen. These fringes are about 65 mm apart and their width almost exactly 1/50th order. This is in harmony with our usual good figure for the width of monochromatic fringes. The fringe width depends on the particular wavelength region and increases towards the blue, since the reflectivity of silver diminishes with the wavelength. The picture shows (*a*) polish scratch marks, and (*b*) a second-order waviness, with wavelength of about 0·1 mm and height, perhaps half a fringe width, say 25 Å.

Attention is drawn to the great magnification in Plate 16. The two fringes correspond to a height change of half a light wave, say $2 \cdot 5 \times 10^{-5}$ cm, but are actually 65 mm apart so that the magnification is *260,000 times*.

(7) An extremely valuable property of these fringes is the un-ambiguous way in which discontinuous steps can be evaluated and the directions of the steps determined, simultaneously. Consider for example Plate 17 ($\times$ 10). This shows the fringes of equal chromatic order given by a thin sheet of high-quality mica which has been silvered on both sides. The fringes appear in pairs and these can be shown to be plane polarized mutually perpendicularly. (This is because mica is birefringent so that μ has two values, one for the extraordinary and one for the ordinary ray.) The smooth straight parallelism of the fringes indicates that t is remarkably constant (this will be taken up again later) but the particular point of interest here is the existence of a discontinuous change in thickness, clearly seen, which is due to an abrupt cleavage step. As already pointed out, in monochromatic Fizeau fringes there are difficulties in connection with assessment of such steps. Here all difficulties are resolved in accordance with the following treatment.

Evaluation of the Fringes

Two situations can arise, one in which t is such that the fringes do not differ a great deal in wavelength (as in Plate 14 and Plate 17), and one in which they are so widespread that there may be a mere two or three fringes covering the whole visible spectrum. Phase change can complicate the latter case, but can be ignored in the former which is simpler to treat first.

According to whether the topographical height change is a good deal less than a light wave, or more than a light wave, different methods of calculation are available.

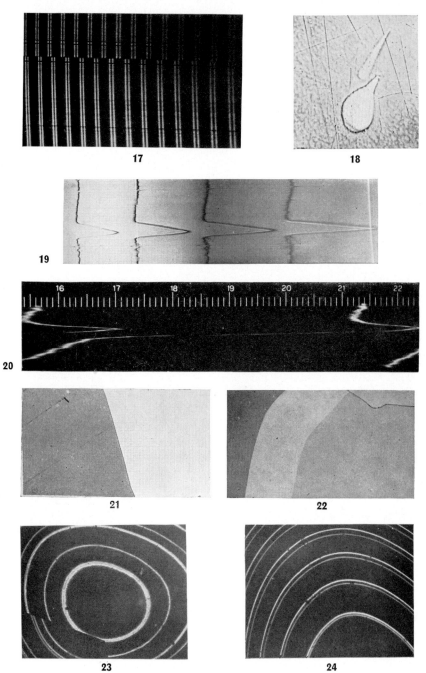

Plates 17-24

If the fringes are not too widespread and if the change in t is small, since $n\lambda = 2t$ then $dn\dfrac{\lambda}{2} = dt$. It is only necessary to measure the fraction of an order separation (by the bracketing method) for wavelength λ to obtain dt. Since $n = 2t/\lambda$, a displacement to the violet (shorter λ) takes place for a smaller t, i.e. for a step *up* towards the optical flat, thus direction is determined also.

In Plate 17 a coincidence method of calculation is applicable. Select any two wavelengths separated by ΔV. Let there be m fringes on the one side of the step (height t_1) and n on the other (height t_2). Neither m nor n need be integers. Then $t_1 = m/2\Delta V$, $t_2 = n/2\Delta V$, whence the step height $t_2 - t_1 = (n - m)/2\Delta V$. The up and down can be determined by mere inspection, the region with the fewer fringes being up, i.e. nearer the matching flat. (When a sheet of mica silvered on both sides is examined, the region with the fewer fringes is the thinner.)

The second case which arises is that in which dispersion is deliberately made high to increase the magnification. This introduces a secondary complication in that the phase change of reflection of light at silver is not quite the same for the different wavelengths of the visible spectrum. In effect the optical spacing differs a little at different wavelengths. A correction is only significant when the surfaces are very close together, i.e. when n is small and the fringes are very widespread. The importance of a phase correction has recently been examined by W. F. Koehler (*J. Opt. Soc. Amer.*, **43**, 738, 1953), and by C. J. Koester (*J. Opt. Soc. Amer.*, **48**, 225, 1958) who also considers refined improvements in the approximations given here. Since in fact the phase change increases effectively linearly with wavelength (it represents an equivalent of some 300 Å over the whole visible region) it turns out that a knowledge of the phase is not required and the step height is given by measuring fringe displacement and two wavelengths. Suppose there are two fringes λ_1 and λ_2. Let the displacement at the λ_1 fringe be $d\lambda_1$, then very closely (to within a few parts in a thousand) the step dt is given by

$$dt = \frac{d\lambda_1}{\lambda_1 - \lambda_2} \cdot \frac{\lambda_2}{2}.$$

Uses of Fringes of Equal Chromatic Order

Problems at times arise when the Fizeau fringe pattern is circular and is less than an order. In this case the fraction of an order is indeterminate with one wavelength. Fringes of equal chromatic order are ideally suited here. They can equally be used in reflection and in transmission. An excellent example of their use in reflection is shown here. Plate 18 (× 70) shows a peculiar growth feature recorded on a synthetic quartz crystal. Fizeau fringes showed that it was a rounded elevation, perhaps half a light wave high. The fringes of equal chromatic order taken with the slit crossing the width of the feature are shown in Plate 19 (× 50). Red is on the left. The feature is a hillock, a little over 2000 Å in height and its shape and profile are clearly rendered. It will be noticed that as one progresses to the violet the fringe occupies a bigger and bigger fraction of an order. This is because whilst the height is a fixed number of ångström units the wavelength is diminishing so that the fringe progressively occupies more and more of an order.

Transmission fringes of *magnification 350,000 times* for a small feature on the surface of a diamond are shown in Plate 20 (× 100) (red at the right). It will be realized that the × 100 magnification refers to linear dimensions in extension, but the × 350,000 refers to height.

The fringes of equal chromatic order give a local line section only, and to survey a complex structure it is necessary to scan the image across the spectroscope slit by traversing the object across the stage on the microscope stand. This can be done visually with rapidity and the regions of interest selected for photography.

Birefringence

Consider the effect of a birefringence, as in Plate 17, which refers to a parallel-sided film of mica. Interference is governed by $n\lambda = 2\mu t$ and now λ and μ are the variables (the μ changing because of birefringence, not because of dispersion, which has a different effect). Differentiating gives $d\lambda = d\mu \dfrac{\lambda}{\mu}$, so that the birefringence $d\mu$ produces a fringe doubling $d\lambda$. A striking feature of this expression is that the wavelength doubling is independent of t, a most unusual effect in interferometry. These fringes enable birefringence values to be derived over the whole visible region from one photograph.

The Optical Flats

The question of the optical flats to be used in most of the work described in this text will now be discussed. Plate 2 and Plate 16 show the admirable quality of a good optical flat. Plate 16 reveals that such a flat also has a secondary structure due to polish marks. Now the employment of a high-grade optical flat has been found *unnecessary*, especially when the microscope is used, which is most frequently the case. For suppose a 1-in. disc of glass is carefully selected to be flat to within one order (and this is not too difficult if a search is made through a stock of glass), then over the region of 1 mm the surface is true to 1/50th of a light wave. One is frequently concerned with a region of only 1/10th mm and by this argument such a region is flat to within $\lambda/500$. Clearly what is now important is not the flatness, but the *smoothness*, i.e. to what extent is there secondary structure?

In the course of our researches we have found two remarkable smooth matching surfaces. The first is *fire-polished* glass (*not* mechanically polished). This may well be curved, but, when selected, shows remarkable smoothness. The second is selected mica, which can be smooth to within molecular dimensions over even some *square centimetres*. (Some other crystals show locally very smooth regions also molecularly true, as will be demonstrated later, but these are not of general applicability as reference surfaces.)

Consider first the mica. Attention is drawn to the remarkable smooth quality of the fringes obtained in Plate 17 by silvering both sides of a selected piece of mica. This shows both that the thickness is uniform and that the two surfaces are highly perfect locally, down to molecular dimensions as will soon be demonstrated. By no means all micas exhibit this perfection. After surveying numerous micas from a variety of origins the best we have found optically is muscovite from the Rex Mine, Alice Springs, Central Australia.

When a thin sheet of such a mica is silvered on both sides and viewed in parallel light from an *unfiltered* mercury arc, large areas of uniform tint appear. Two such areas are shown in Plates 21 and 22 ($\times$ 5). It is with areas such as these that one obtains the straight parallel fringes of Plate 17. Now this uniformity in tint is a highly critical test of perfection both of uniformity of thickness and of surface smoothness in accordance with the following argument.

Suppose two flat parallel silvered plates are illuminated at normal incidence with parallel monochromatic light. Then the transmitted intensity obeys the Airy relation $I = \dfrac{I_0}{1 + F \sin^2 \delta/2}$. In this instance $\dfrac{\delta}{2} = \dfrac{2\pi t}{\lambda}$. If one plate is moved parallel to itself then there results an intensity variation with t which follows the familiar distribution shown in Fig. 24, in which intensity I is now plotted against thickness t. Now visualize a stepped system as in Fig. 25 in which one plate has a step on it dt. Clearly, the intensity transmitted by the left and right halves A and B will differ. As to how much they differ depends upon where one is situated within the intensity distribution of Fig. 24, i.e. upon t. If situated within the region of the peak, X, a small change in t makes a *big* change in I and conversely if situated within the region of the minimum Y a big change in t makes very *little* change in I. It is self-evident from symmetry considerations that a given change in t causes a maximum change in I if one selects a region near to half the maximum, as is clear from Fig. 26. This is because of the advantageous steep shape of the intensity curve.

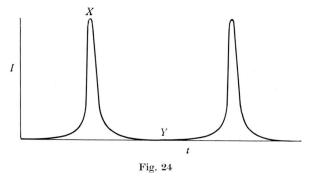

Fig. 24

It will be assumed that the eye or photographic plate can distinguish a 10% change in intensity, which is reasonable. The change dt, at the favourable position required to produce this is readily computed. Writing $\delta = 4\pi t/\lambda$ where t now refers to the half-intensity position, this

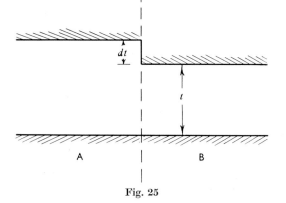

Fig. 25

occurs at a phase δ such that $\dfrac{I_0}{2} = \dfrac{I_0}{1 + F \sin^2 \delta/2}$. As δ is small it can replace its sine such that $\delta = \dfrac{2}{F^{1/2}}$. Now the next region at t' is to differ

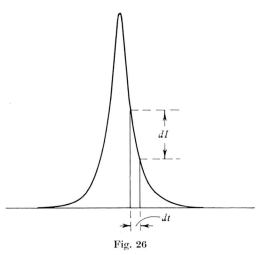

Fig. 26

in intensity by 10%, i.e. intensity is $\dfrac{I_0}{2}(1 \pm 0\cdot1)$. For this computation it matters little whether one takes an increase or a decrease of 10%. Selecting a decrease, then the phase position δ' for the separation t' is given by $0\cdot45\,I_0 = \dfrac{I_0}{1 + F\sin^2\delta'/_2}$ which gives $\delta' = \dfrac{2\cdot21}{F^{1/2}}$. Thus as $\delta' - \delta = \dfrac{4\pi}{\lambda}(t' - t)$, the detectable 10% change in intensity is pro-

duced by a change in separation $dt = t' - t = \dfrac{\lambda}{4\pi}(\delta' - \delta)$, i.e. $\dfrac{\lambda}{4\pi}\dfrac{0\cdot21}{F^{1/2}}$. Closely enough this is $\dfrac{\lambda}{60F^{1/2}}$. Taking the green mercury line $\lambda = 5\cdot4 \times 10^{-5}$ cm, then $dt = \dfrac{9 \times 10^{-7}}{F^{1/2}}$ cm. The sensitivity is then determined by $F^{1/2}\left(\text{which equals }\dfrac{2R^{1/2}}{1 - R}\right)$, i.e. it depends only on reflectivity. A value of $R = 0\cdot95$ can be obtained for which $F^{1/2}$ is 36 whereby $dt = 2\cdot5 \times 10^{-8}$ cm, i.e. 2·5 Å.

This is a remarkable and unexpected result for it shows that in the fringe pattern a change of height of a mere 2·5 Å, *which is less than many molecular crystal lattice spacings*, produces 10% change of intensity. The unexpected sensitivity of this type of interference contrast can be indicated in another manner. The crystal lattice spacing between mica cleavage planes is 20 Å. If one writes $dt = 20$ Å, then dI is some 50%.

Thus a cleavage step of a *single* molecular lattice will produce as much as 50% change in intensity. Of course this is true only at the optimum position of t. In general, t will be off the optimum therefore it is desirable to use several wavelengths. This adds further to visual sensitivity in two ways. First, it increases the chances of being near the optimum, second it leads to subtle colour tint changes when the step height changes. The eye is particularly sensitive to such subtle colour changes. Referring back to Plates 21 and 22 it is seen that these large areas must be actually true to within a single crystal lattice spacing, for they are of quite uniform tint.

The surfaces, although molecularly smooth, are by no means flat. The mica sheet is wrinkled, like a crumpled sheet of paper, with hillocks on one side matched by exactly complementary valleys on the other. For all mica sheets invariably give a hill-dale topography when matched against a flat.

A sheet of mica can be used as a reference to examine local smoothness and local microstructure if the defect of its hill-dale pattern is recognized as present. Thus W. L. Wilcock made the following experiment. Plate 23 (× 10) shows the fringe pattern given by two pieces of selected mica silvered and pressed face to face. The fringes are curved, but are perfectly smooth. There is no evidence at all of any microstructure. One of these mica pieces was next matched against a piece of selected fire-polished glass, the interferogram being shown in Plate 24 (× 10). Very little structure appears indeed although in the original photograph it can be seen that the fringes are slightly granulated. The granulation merely broadens the fringe and introduces an occasional wriggle, but there is hardly any resolvable structure. Such interferograms confirm the smooth character of the fire-polished glass surfaces which have been used systematically in the work described here. It is as if when the liquid glass surface froze it retained the smooth character of a liquid.

The Testing of Multilayers

Fringes of equal chromatic order offer a rapid method for locating the wavelength maximum peak of high reflectivity for multilayers. It is only necessary to place close together two glass plates coated with the multilayers and then examine the fringes of equal chromatic order with a small constant-deviation wavelength scale spectrometer. Because of the chromaticity variation in reflectivity the fringes are sharp only in a restricted wavelength band and broaden up very rapidly on either side of this. The central wavelength region, that of optimum reflectivity, can be read off on the wavelength drum and it is thereby quickly decided whether the multilayer is suited for Fizeau fringes, using a line of a predetermined wavelength.

REFERENCES

Nos. 8, 10, 22.

4. CROSSED FRINGES

Crossed Fizeau Fringes—References.

Crossed Fizeau Fringes

THE method of crossed Fizeau fringes is a multiple-beam interference technique of considerable elegance and highly economical in the information content offered on a single photograph. It is applicable to transparent materials, and requires that there should be available a region which is reasonably flat overall, although on this relatively flat region it is the microstructure which is under examination. Accordingly, the magnification which can be used depends upon the extent of reasonably flat area that is available. For example on one particularly fine flat diamond (such diamonds are called portrait stones) almost 1 sq cm was open to the technique, whereas on another stone only 1 sq mm was suitable. Consider the multiple-beam Fizeau picture, Plate 25 ($\times$ 35), taken over a natural untouched octahedral face on a fine flat diamond (portrait stone). A mercury-arc source was used with a yellow filter which transmitted with about equal intensity the two yellow and the green mercury lines. Fringes appear in groups of three. The wedge is opening out from top right-hand to bottom left-hand corner. The two yellow lines are close together at the top and open up to the bottom. The green line is perhaps a quarter of an order away at the top and has caught up with the yellow pair and indeed overlaps at the bottom right.

It is clear that there is some sort of complex topography on this surface yet the very excellent fringe definition is actually a drawback. For the total area covered by fringes is only a small fraction of the area under study, and if a detailed survey of the whole topography is needed then perhaps fifty to a hundred such interferograms would be required, and a formidable problem emerges of the synthesis from all these patterns, placed at different positions to cover the entire area.

The crossed-fringe system solves this problem on a single photograph and furthermore offers a very vivid three-dimensional picture of the topography. It is based on the following considerations. In Plate 25 the silvered optical flat makes a wedge angle with the silvered diamond. If this wedge angle is reduced, and provided the surface microtopography is such as to permit a near enough approach to parallelism,

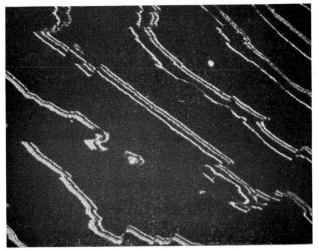

25

26

Plates 25, 26

then the fringe pattern broadens out. If several wavelengths are included in the source, the interference pattern obtained becomes that shown in Plate 26. This is full of structural detail and is an optical system in which there is what can be called a very high *interference contrast*. The optical properties of such a system have already been reviewed when discussing the use of doubly-silvered mica, where it was shown that a local height change of a mere $2\frac{1}{2}$ Å can produce a local 10% change in intensity, when the optical conditions are suitable. Plate 26 is a microphotograph with *interference contrast* which compares very favourably even with the best phase contrast. The difference between this and phase-contrast is worthy of note. Phase contrast operates through diffraction and shows up best at sharp *edges and ridges*, interference contrast, on the other hand, reveals *extended areas* which differ in height. As the high sensitivity is localized within the region of the fringe maximum it is decidedly advantageous to use several wavelengths, such that if t is not correct for one wavelength it may be correct for another. An unfiltered mercury arc is suitable ; still better is a mercury arc with a small quantity of cadmium or zinc added.

Although the interferogram on Plate 26 is of very high contrast sensitivity, it is not usable for exact measurements for two reasons. The first is that changes in intensity are notoriously difficult to assess. Second, the same change in intensity is produced by an alteration in height of dt and equally by $dt \pm n\lambda/2$ in which n can have any integral value. The method of crossed fringes solves the whole difficulty. It is desirable to use a microscope which has on its camera attachment a viewing eye-piece which can be introduced or withdrawn at will without disturbing the photographic plate. This is standard laboratory equipment.

The dispersion of the interferometric system is first arranged to give Plate 25 and an exposure is made. The plate is left untouched in the camera and the optical flat is then adjusted to give the fringe pattern of Plate 26. This is then registered in superposition on the same photographic plate, without moving the latter. On development of the plate, this shows the crossed-fringe pattern of Plate 27 ($\times$ 35). This remarkable picture offers at once a mass of topographical information, for the two fringe systems ideally complement each other. The meanderings and twistings of the fringes of Plate 25 acquire now an obvious physical meaning, clearly revealing growth sheets and other numerous features. Conversely, the broad contrast-sensitive fringes of Plate 26 now become amenable to precise numerical evaluation and interpretation. The vivid way in which a growth pyramid is revealed over the lower right

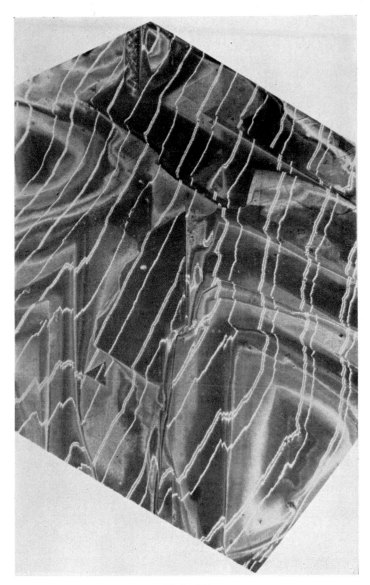

Plate 27

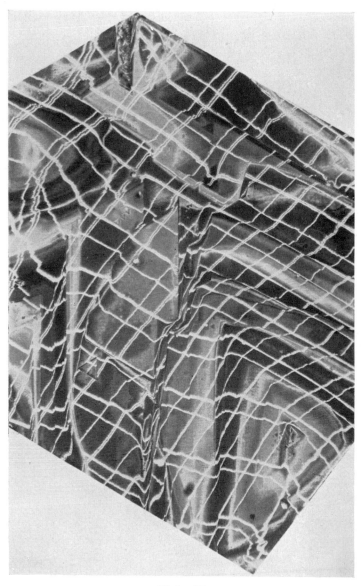

Plate 28

region on Plate 27 needs no detailed emphasis, but there are numerous other features of obvious interest.

Thus for instance in the dark regions which correspond to the position Y on Fig. 24 there is no contrast sensitivity and one sees the narrow fringes wriggling and changing with no alteration at all in the background. But in the bright regions, (i.e. within interference maxima) the extreme sensitivity is readily apparent. A small fringe kink, *a matter of a mere few ångström units in height*, is linked with a very strong change in brightness. A small alteration of adjustment in the tilt of the optical flat easily changes over the positions of brightness and darkness. Indeed no two photographs under high dispersion are ever quite alike.

One can go a step further and employ *doubly-crossed* fringes by setting *two separate* sets of linear fringes more or less at right angles superposed on the high dispersion system. This is shown in Plate 28 (× 35) which, it will be seen, contains a most comprehensive topographical analysis of the crystal surface.

The value of the crossed fringes in assisting topographical interpretation is rendered clear by consideration of the well-marked triangular depression at the bottom left in Plate 27. These triangular pits, called trigons, are usually found on octahedral diamond faces.

Another crossed-fringe picture of this region is shown in Plate 29 (× 180). Referring back to Plate 27, first it will be noticed that the level within the trigon is the same as that of the extended region outside. The position is clear. A fringe comes down a region which is almost a true plane, since the fringe is so straight and its neighbours are equally straight and parallel, apart from small local disturbances. The fringe then reaches a shelf with a curved edge and moves to the right. Measurement shows that the shelf height is some 400 Å. But note that the fringe *within* the trigon is a linear continuation of the outer straight fringe, which establishes that the *base* of the triangle is *coplanar* with the outer region. Exact measurement shows that the two fringes are colinear to within 10 Å and it must not be forgotten that such differences can be introduced by the matching flat. It is certain that they are coplanar to within very few single crystal lattices and may well be coincident *to within one and the same lattice spacing*. This clearly sheds light on the origin of formation of such flat-based trigons about which much will be said later. If the shelf region has grown by plane wave fronts which are inclined to each other at 60° then any interruption in growth will lead to an equiangular triangular depression and this would have its base at the same level as some outer region.

The use of the crossed-fringe technique is well demonstrated by the

29

30

31

Plates 29-31

following further example, obtained with a remarkable flat diamond some 5 mm in length. Two crossed-fringe patterns are shown in Plates 30 and 31 ($\times$ 40) and these are instructive. It is seen that there exist two areas with an astonishing degree of plane perfection separated in height by about 900 Å. The crossed fringes have been arranged to run at right angles in the two pictures. The plane perfection of the two surfaces is unique, amongst many thousands of different crystal surfaces examined in my laboratory during the past fifteen years.

The background is mottled and high magnification shows there is a mass of extremely shallow small trigons on this. It will be established later that such trigons can be of depth of perhaps but a single lattice, and such shallow features can account both for the mottling and the slight wrinkles in the otherwise straight fringes.

Plane surfaces reveal themselves by exhibiting straight parallel equidistant fringes and on Plate 30 and Plate 31 there is practically no detectable difference in order spacings in the flat regions.

Instructive is the fact that in Plate 31 the high-dispersion high-contrast background is in the sensitive setting, whilst in Plate 30 it is otherwise. How sensitive it is, is shown by the narrow strips at the bottom left of the left-hand plane region, wherein marked intensity changes are shown by one step which is a mere 20 Å in height (Plate 31).

It is unfortunate that this unique crystal, which was examined in 1945, was called in by the diamond organization and lost its way into industry before a more detailed study was undertaken. The surfaces were natural-growth octahedra. A crystal of such perfection of finish would have been worthy of a general physical examination, electrical, thermal, optical and mechanical. The tabular regions shown were the high regions and the rough stepped region at the bottom of the pictures was a descent down.

REFERENCES

Nos. 11, 18, 22, F.

5. THICKNESS OF THIN FILMS

Measurement of thickness of thin films—References.

Measurement of Thickness of Thin Films

WHILST a knowledge of the thickness of the thin films used in interferometry is not really essential, it is of interest to point out that the multiple-beam fringe systems can be used for evaluating the thicknesses of thin films in general. Indeed they have been used by numerous experimenters for this particular purpose. Such an application is valuable in many experiments although of course it is not as exciting a field of investigation as that of microtopography. Nor does it offer such a challenge to the experimenter. The multiple-beam method of measuring film thickness will now be reviewed. Either multiple-beam Fizeau fringes or fringes of equal chromatic order can be adopted.

Although electron microscopy shows that thin metallic films have a granular structure, such films can be considered continuous from the viewpoint of optical microscopy. As thin films are an important object of study in numerous fields of scientific research, much attention has been devoted to the measurement of thin film thickness. An early and difficult method was that which used the micro-balance. The weight of a known area of metal deposited was determined and it was then assumed that the density of the metal in the thin film is that of bulk metal, so that from the area the thickness can be computed. For extremely thin layers the density assumption may be invalid, especially for films below 100 Å thick. It is claimed that with the micro-balance thickness can be determined to within an error of some 10 or 20 Å.

In special instances, such as silver, chemical methods for estimating the mass of metal in a thin film have been developed. These can be quite accurate but, of course, the film under study is destroyed and it is necessary to measure a monitor film instead of that to be used. Another method involves chemical transformation of the metal into a transparent dielectric and then evaluation of the thickness of the thin dielectric film with a Jamin or like interferometer. There are several difficulties in interpretation in this method.

Wiener (*Wied. Ann.*, **31**, 629, 1887) proposed a two-beam Fizeau fringe interferometric method for measuring thin film thickness. It is this early approach which has been adapted and considerably modified and improved by multiple-beam methods. In these newer techniques, developed in my laboratory, special attention has been paid to phase problems and both Fizeau systems and fringes of equal chromatic order have been adopted. The techniques have established themselves as consistent and reliable.

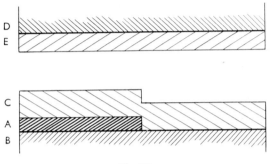

Fig. 27

The interferometric method is illustrated in Fig. 27. Let the film to be studied, A, be deposited on a smooth glass substrate B. It should cover part of the glass and end with a sharp edge. This is achieved by masking the glass with a sheet of mica. Then over the compound surface of A-B is deposited an opaque film of silver, C, about 1000 Å thick. As will be shown later, it has been adequately demonstrated that such an overlay film of 1000 Å accurately contours the underlying surface so that a step appears in C which is equal to the metrical thickness of A. Another smooth glass flat D, with the usual reflecting film E for reflection interferometry, is matched against the lower system and illuminated from above in parallel monochromatic light for multiple-beam Fizeau fringes. The fringes between the surfaces E and C reveal the step height A which can be accurately measured.

The fringes should be set normal to the step edge for convenience in measurement. Plate 32 (× 10) shows the pattern for a relatively large step, 1520 Å, and it can be seen from the fine definition that high accuracy is attainable. Plate 33 (× 10) shows a step of 214 Å and Plate 34 (× 10) a step of 66 Å. The accuracy in measurement is high (some ± 3 Å) and it is clear from Plate 34 that a step as small as 20 Å can be measured.

High dispersion and high resolving power can be obtained by using fringes of equal chromatic order. Plate 35 (× 40) shows high dispersion fringes with only two fringes in the whole visible region. The step height in this instance is 480 Å. The fringes in the red are 10 mm apart and are but half a mm wide. One can certainly measure a step which is only some 1/20th of this separation.

It can be considered certain that the multiple-beam method is good enough for measuring film thickness down to 20 Å. Fringes of equal chromatic order are preferable for the thinnest films, the Fizeau fringes being best for the thicker films.

The fringe system is *viewed in reflection* from above, and the opaque film C plays an important role. To begin with, it has maximum reflectivity and thus extremely fine fringes are secured. Secondly, it overcomes phase effects in accordance with the following considerations. When light is reflected from a composite surface such as glass, covered half-way with metal, i.e. A-B, not only is there a path difference due to the thickness of A, there is also a phase difference because B is glass and A is metal. To complicate matters the phase change from A depends on the thickness of A itself in an unknown way. Now the phase effect from a thin metal layer rapidly approaches the constant value characteristic of bulk metal when the film thickness increases until it approaches opacity. In fact for a film thickness of some 700 Å (for silver) the phase change is that of bulk metal. Clearly, the phase change for the beams reflected from the two parts of the lower composite system are now the same ; they are that of bulk silver provided C is some 1000 Å. The film A does not have any effect on phase now and only the metrical height is registered interferometrically.

For this, and other, reasons it is *undesirable* to attempt to make the measurement in transmission by making C sufficiently thin to transmit light. For then there would be the difference in phase in transmission between two transparent films of different thickness, the one a simple silver film, the other the composite (C + A) film. Again, if A is of appreciable thickness there would also be a difference in fringe *width*. For example : let A be, say, 500 Å then a value of C more than 200 Å cannot be tolerated, otherwise AC becomes opaque. So on the left AC is a film of thickness 700 Å which has a good reflectivity, but on the right CB is merely 200 Å thick and consequently is a very poor reflector. As a result the left-side fringes are very sharp and the right side very broad, making accurate measurement impossible.

The advantages of making C equal to 1000 Å and operating in reflection are now self evident. The film A can be of any material, metal or dielectric, and indeed the method is of general applicability.

Whilst it is evident that interferometry permits valuation of a measurable step height of some 20 Å, the question must be considered as to the true physical interpretation of the measurements on the extremely thin films. One experiment was made which indicates the difficulties involved when considering the very thin films. The question to be examined was that of the existence of any granulosity effect and the following was tried. A silver film was deposited over half a glass plate X and simultaneously over one-half of another glass plate Y which had been first pre-coated with 1000 Å of silver. The film thickness on X was determined, as usual, by coating with 1000 Å of silver, but the film thickness on Y could be determined directly without any overcoating.

This experiment was repeated for a whole series of film thicknesses and the compared experimental values from X and Y are shown below (data are in ångströms) :

Film thickness on X	Film thickness on Y
750	752
358	363
269	270
100	100
67	67
15	29

Down to a film thickness of 67 Å there is effectively complete identity between the two sets X and Y. There is clear failure below this. Plate 36 (× 70) shows fringe patterns for the thinnest film deposited on to silver, and Plate 37 (× 70) for that on to glass. The apparent difference is clear. It seems a reasonable conclusion that the thin film on the glass is so loosely granular that the overcoat beds-in and is partly lost, so that too thin a film appears to be registered. The evidence strongly suggests that the technique is adequate down to about 50 Å, but is suspect below this.

We have explored the character of our silver films with an electron microscope and this exactly confirms this conclusion. Silver films of different thicknesses were all prepared under, as far as possible, identical vacuum conditions and grown at the rate of 20 Å per second. Replica electron micrographs were secured at a uniform magnification of × 45,000. Plates 38, 39, 40, 41, 42 (× 45,000) show parts of electron micrographs for film thickness of 20, 38, 60, 87, and 130 Å respectively.

At 20 Å the surface of the silver consists of discrete granules. At 38 Å these are running into each other and at 60 Å have effectively come into contact. By 87 Å the surface is more uniform. By 130 Å there is

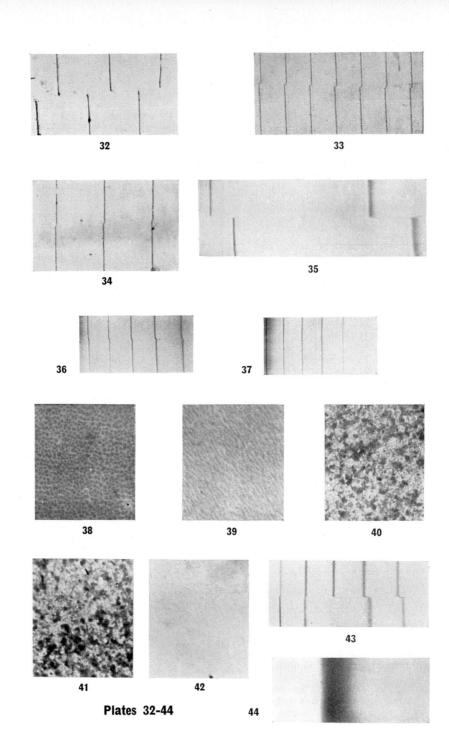

32

33

34

35

36

37

38

39

40

41

42

43

44

Plates 32-44

effective uniformity, with numerous long narrow cracks, which separate very uniform regions, the cracks themselves occupying only a small fraction of the total area.

It is evident from these excellent high magnification micrographs that somewhere between 40 and 60 Å the granules unite. This is in exact agreement with the conclusion drawn from interferometry. Thus it is reiterated that interferometric thin-film measurement in the general case can be relied on down to 50 Å. Below this it is suspect, unless the film is first put down on to a pre-coated silvered surface. This means that the technique can then really only be soundly extended below 50 Å for *silver* films, for clearly deposit of any other metal than silver on top of silver at once raises phase change problems. For silver films, using this modification, it should be possible to measure films as thin as 20 Å.

We have explored the possibility of using a multilayer on top of a thin film instead of silver, i.e. replacing the silver overcoating by a multilayer overcoating. The result has been unexpected and surprising. Consider fringes in transmission first. The thin film being measured was 750 Å thick and a transparent overcoating consisting of a 7-component multilayer was deposited on this. The multilayer therefore coated both silver and glass. A multilayer has no effective absorption. On the matching flat was also a multilayer. The fringes of equal chromatic order in transmission given by this system are shown in Plate 43 and these have most peculiar characteristics. Plates 43 and 44 are both positives. The upper half of Plate 43 is the system multilayer against multilayer and has a region of sharp fringes where reflectivity is high, i.e. at the correct wavelength region which is near the green. (It is a matter of accidental dispersion as to whether or not a fringe appears very close to the exact wavelength for peak reflectivity.) The lower half in Plate 43 shows the fringe system silver + multilayer matched against multilayer. This is most unusual. To begin with the region of sharpest fringes has moved well over to the red end of the spectrum (the left). Starting from the red, the lower fringes are displaced to the *red* and then the fringe expected near 5100 is missing, or at least there is only a faint broad patch here. The next fringe (still broad) displaces to the *blue* and successive fringes sharpen up. The interference system was dismantled and white light reflected in a spectrograph from the compound surface silver + multilayer. The spectral distribution of the reflected light is shown in Plate 44. It is clear that the combination is acting as an *anti-reflection coating* in the very region where the fringe is missing, since no light is reflected here (Plate 44 is a positive). This, of course, entirely explains the absence of that fringe. Further, the anti-reflection effect partially spreads out to the violet and this again explains the broadened fringes in the combination fringe pattern.

All this is due to a complex phase change effect which seems to take place at the silver-multilayer interface, an effect which is a function of the wavelength and which is a maximum in the wavelength region for which the multilayer has its optimum reflectivity.

It is quite evident that multilayers cannot as yet be used as over-coatings for film thickness determinations. A good deal more exploration on these peculiar properties is required before this can be done.

REFERENCES

Nos. 22, 30, T.

PART TWO

TOPOGRAPHIES OF CRYSTAL FACES

6. TOPOGRAPHIES OF DIAMOND FACES

Preliminary—Octahedral faces—Trigons—Dodecahedral faces—References.

The Topography of Crystal Faces, Preliminary

Now that some of the more important techniques of multiple-beam interferometry have been described (several others have been developed too) the text following will be devoted to the illustration of a wide variety of applications of these methods to the study of surface microtopographies. These studies will be divided into broad sections. This first section will deal with the study of natural faces of some crystals and then with the examination of several types of crystal cleavage. Later sections will deal in turn with etching of crystals, oscillating quartz crystals, finish of machined metals, studies on hardness, deformations of surfaces, and some other aspects.

This begins with a study of natural diamond faces.

Diamonds: Octahedral Faces

Some of the most striking observations on microtopographies of crystals with multiple-beam methods have been obtained on diamonds. Already some interferograms on diamond have been shown when describing the crossed-fringe technique. We have devoted much attention to diamond for a number of reasons. It is a unique material. Its outstanding hardness makes it of considerable importance as a technological material for cutting, grinding, drilling and polishing other hard materials. It is prized as a gem stone and has a long history as such. Curious problems arise in connection with the fabrication of diamond, which is only possible because certain directions are less resistant to abrasion than others. It is easily cleaved or cracked and we have established that crystallographically oriented percussion marks can be induced very easily on diamond faces.

As a crystal, it is of great interest and much has been written about the genesis of diamond in the earth. Its unique hardness makes it an ideal material for microtopographic studies, since leeching processes do not damage a diamond surface at all and, furthermore, when extracted from its natural ores it is certain that the observed structure is effectively the original structure at cessation of growth. For water solution has no effect at all and any abrasions to which it has been subject will not have influenced the surface structure. (This is not to be expected for diamonds from alluvial sources which might have been subject to prolonged abrasive action.

Natural diamonds occur in a variety of forms and, of these, two types dominate—the octahedron, often with fairly flat sides, and the dodecahedron, frequently with strongly curved faces. Cubes at times turn up and, of course, there are many intermediate forms between these. In general the octahedra show on their surfaces beautifully clear small equiangular depressions, now called *trigons*, which are oriented such that the points of the trigons point towards the *edges* of the octahedron faces, which are themselves triangular. It is my belief that *all* octahedra exhibit trigons and a case for this will be established later, wherein it will be shown that trigons are a basic growth mechanism.

The dodecahedral faces have at times striations, at times a curious network, which it will be shown is probably due to etch processes. Cleavage faces have a character of their own and these too have been studied and discussed.

In different mines there is a differential preponderance of octahedroid and dodecahedroid types, the one type predominating in some mines, the other in others. Octahedra frequently occur in flat forms, of which there are two different kinds, both of which are often well suited to study by interferometry. The one kind is called a *portrait stone* and it occurs as a flat effectively plane-parallel thin slab of hexagonal outline. This comes about through overdevelopment of two opposite octahedron faces, and the edges of the hexagon are the remaining octahedron faces. A stone like this is ideally suited for transmission fringe studies. The orientation of the trigons on viewing through the stone appears opposite on the two opposite plane faces. The other flat type is the triangular plate twin form called a ' macle ', which appears as a thick triangular plate with a twinning plane parallel to the plane of the triangular faces, which are octahedron faces. The portrait stone, so called because large good examples were used as windows to cover miniature portraits painted on ivory, are sometimes found of very fine quality, and some of the studies reported here have been made with such fine-quality stones. Many diamonds have extremely rough surfaces, but the stones described here have been carefully selected for their relative perfection in order to enable the high precision techniques to be fully deployed.

Trigons. A typically good octahedron face will reveal by multiple-beam interferometry a pattern like Plate 45 (× 35). A part of this region at higher magnification (× 170) is shown in Plate 46. These interferograms indicate how considerable information can be secured in a qualitative manner without even measurements. It is seen that trigons are of two types, those which are relatively fairly deep and those which are very shallow. There is a curious statistic in that the dimensions within the two types, both in extension and in depth, do not cover a very great range.

Consider the three larger trigons on the left in Plate 46. The following can be assessed at a glance. Their depths are readily estimated, since each fringe corresponds to a depth of $\lambda/2$ (green mercury). The two upper trigons descend to a pyramidal point, the lower has a flat base. The nearly equidistant fringe spacing within the sides of the lower trigon indicate a plane slope, whereas the differential spacing in the middle trigon indicates the existence of a concave curvature. On the right the high interference contrast reveals shallower trigons within shallow trigons. It is not the purpose here to analyse the vast multiplicities of trigons observed, but to illustrate techniques, so that selected examples will merely be chosen at random from many hundreds of available interferograms which show how complex the diamond topographies can be and how powerfully the fringe systems reveal them.

An example of a fairly flat surface with trigons distributed on it is shown in Plate 47 (× 30).

Although the shallow trigons have strictly linear outline, crossed fringes reveal in a striking way one especial characteristic often found, namely an asymmetry in the *surrounding* surface. This is shown to advantage by Plate 48 (× 100). Here is a crossed fringe system in which trigons appear to sit on line discontinuities. This is not uncommon and it is almost certainly a line dislocation on which the trigon sits. The crossed fringes near the large dark main trigon show clearly the mechanism of growth. The growth sheets have progressed from below and halted at the dislocation. They sweep round and the incompletion leaves the trigon but the sweep round leads to a slowing down in growth rate, as shown by the way the fringe dips in, to show a curved drop towards the trigon.

This mechanism is shown even to better advantage by Plate 49 (× 50) which is a high-contrast, sensitive, high-dispersion interferogram at optimal sensitivity. The curved dips surrounding the dislocation bases on which the trigons sit are vividly rendered by contrast changes. Attention is once more drawn to the striking sensitivity of the interfero-

45

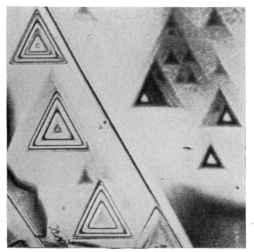

46

47

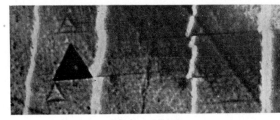

48

Plates 45-48

grams. The relatively large curved drop in Plate 48 is a mere 100 Å or so, and of course, far less would be detectable.

Whereas the trigons are all shallow depressions, there are on many diamonds oppositely oriented *growth pyramids*, built up of plane sheets. A particularly noteworthy example is shown in Plate 50 ($\times$ 100). That such growth hillocks are opposite in orientation to the trigons can be seen on the high-sensitive high-dispersion interferogram shown in Plate 51 ($\times$ 100), which shows part of a very fine portrait stone. Here the high-contrast high-dispersion technique is being employed, for the height is small. The separate discrete growth sheets are visible and a mass of tiny *oppositely* oriented growth trigons can be identified. That this whole surface is covered with shallow small trigons is shown by a section at high magnification in Plate 52 ($\times$ 500). The next interferogram Plate 53 ($\times$ 200) taken over this same surface is of considerable interest in that it shows how valuable numerical data can be secured merely from the character of a *single fringe*. The dispersion is arranged to be high, intermediate between the normal dispersion used for sharp narrow fringes and that used for very broad high-dispersion fringes. Now, with the high reflectivity used, the true fringe width in terms of ångström units is small, being about 1/50th order, i.e. it represents some 50 Å. But it can be seen that the fringe has a serrated structure because of the shallow surface trigons. Clearly some trigon depths are even less than a fifth of one fringe width, i.e. less than 10 Å. None is displaced by more than half the fringe width (25 Å). So the very character of the fringe shape itself reveals that the whole surface is a complete mass of small shallow trigons. Some are little more than a few lattices in depth. Clearly this is revealing here, from a single fringe, the key mechanism by which the diamond has grown.

There is no doubt that these interferometric studies prove that octahedron faces grow by plane sheets and that incompletion of the sheets leaves the trigons.

Diamonds: Dodecahedral Faces

Although it is not intended here to attempt any analysis of the complex structures observed on the dodecahedral faces of diamond, yet it so happens that the curvature of such surfaces has been exploited to give high-magnification fringes of considerable resolving power in terms of the volume resolvable. A large number of diamond dodecahedral faces have been studied and on these the following features have been recorded : (*a*) striations ; (*b*) irregular networks ; (*c*) crystallographically oriented networks ; (*d*) raised circular discs.

49

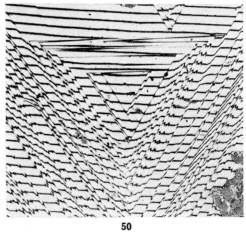

50

51

52

53

Plates 49-53

The striated surfaces are the more frequent and resemble one another. Plate 54 ($\times$ 85) is typical. A high-magnification interferogram of part of this ($\times$ 400) is shown in Plate 55 from which the following information is available. The surface has a marked convex curvature of a cylindrical character. The radius of curvature is readily calculated and is small, of the order of 8 cm. The striations are mostly regular shallow ruts, although there are occasional isolated ridges. Many of the ruts have depth of the order of 500 Å.

The convex, curved nature of these dodecahedral surfaces has enabled us to push the lateral magnification to very high limits by using the following experimental method. The lens used was a 3-mm dry apochromat of N.A. 0·95. This is of the type with a correcting collar for correction due to cover-slip thickness. A selected cover-slip of suitable thickness was used as the optical flat, silvered and mounted against the convex face of the diamond. This permitted *very close approach* and thus, despite the very high magnification, good interferometric fringe definition was secured. Plate 56 ($\times$ 1500) shows the excellent definition obtained by this means. Considering the high magnification of the fringes, sharpness is excellent.

The power of this approach is shown to even better advantage on the oriented networks which have been found on several dodecahedral faces. These networks are intriguing and on a small scale. Plate 57 ($\times$ 1500) is typical and it is seen that the structure consists of a set of strictly oriented parallelograms. An interferogram ($\times$ 250) of part of such a face is shown in Plate 58. We see that there is again an overall cylindrical curvature and at the centre of the system the high dispersion gives effectively a high contrast interference picture. Plate 59 ($\times$ 1500) shows again the result obtained with the 3-mm lens and selected cover-slip. The fringe system is arranged to give part of the central (zero order) patch and the two first complete orders. The fringes show that the parallelogram elements are concave units surrounded by sharp ridges and they give evidence of some solution effect.

As the magnification is high, the elements are actually very highly curved and radii of curvature of the order of from 0·7 to 0·02 mm have been computed.

The parallelogram regions enclose angles of approximately 70° and 110° and their areas range from 5×10^{-8} to 2×10^{-6} sq cm.

It is of much interest to calculate the volume resolution available. The theoretical resolving power of an objective of N.A. = 0·95, when used with parallel incident light of wavelength $5 \cdot 4 \times 10^{-5}$ cm is $3 \cdot 3 \times 10^{-5}$ cm. At magnification $\times$ 1500 this is half a millimetre or so.

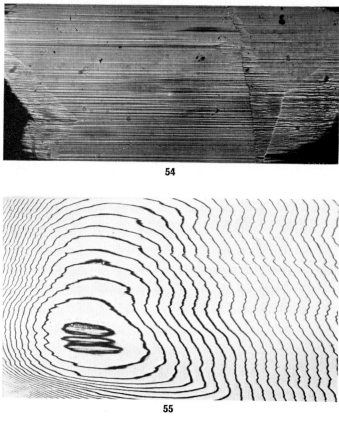

54

55

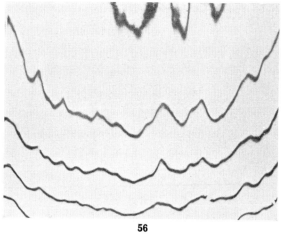

56

Plates 54-56

We are undoubtedly well within tolerance by taking twice this as a safe figure, i.e. $6 \cdot 6 \times 10^{-5}$ cm. Fringe width is experimentally about 1/25th order, i.e. about 100 Å. Our normal practice is to assume that a fifth of a fringe width can be resolved, but again, to be safe in tolerance we shall limit resolution to half a fringe width (50 Å), i.e. to a 1-mm displacement on the picture. This is certainly very tolerant.

The volume element resolvable is then some $(6 \cdot 6 \times 10^{-5})^2 \times 5 \times 10^{-7}$ cc, i.e. about 2×10^{-15} cc. This seems to be near the ultimate attainable limit with multiple-beam interferometry.

Attention is drawn to noticeable difference in width and definition between the first- and second-order fringes. The reason is this. For the first fringe the separation between the surfaces is $\lambda/2$ and for the second it is λ. The surface between the fringes can be treated as a wedge of large angle, interferometrically (at least $1°$), and the increase in separation is sufficient to increase the phase effect such that there is appreciable difference between the definition of the first and second order.

The calculation made for the limit of resolvable small element applies strictly to the first order only, for it is only here that the definition is so superb, at least it is superb when related to the high lateral magnification used.

These two examples suggest that if the highest powers are required in the study of fairly flat surfaces, then instead of using an optical flat one should use, if available, a regularly curved either spherical or cylindrical surface. This approach has not yet been explored by us. Examination of polished lenses reveals inevitable scratches, but it is likely that a suitable reference surface may be secured from fire-polished cylinders of large diameter.

Although some remarkable complex patterns have been discovered on dodecahedra, it will suffice to complete this section by illustrations of the way in which interferometry gives topographical information about selected features. One dodecahedron shows a network and on this is superposed unusual chains of etch pits, in circular arrays. An example is shown in Plate 60 ($\times 95$). An interferogram of a similar region is shown with high magnification in Plate 61 ($\times 100$). This shows up clearly that the pits are flat-bottomed and some are as much as five light waves deep; say 1/400th mm. There is furthermore a marked asymmetry in the slope of the sides, as revealed by the different packing of the fringes. The angles of slope are high, perhaps $5°$, on the steep sides of the pits.

Not all networks are linear oriented patterns and some of the irregular

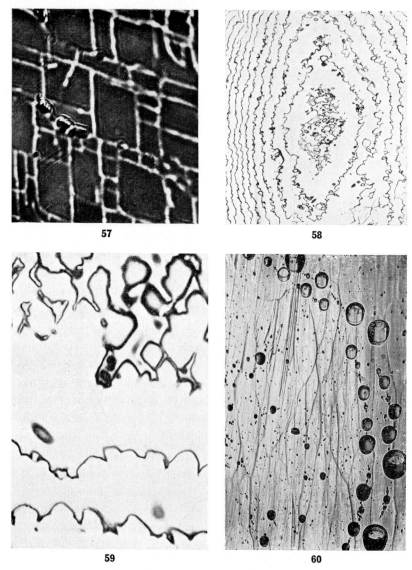

57

58

59

60

61

Plates 57-61

62

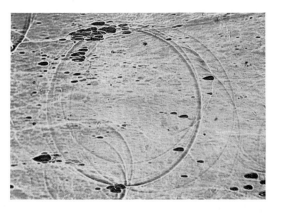

63

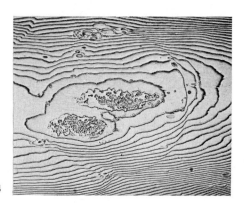

64

Plates 62-64

kind are also clearly visible on Plate 60. A high-definition interferogram over such networks is shown in Plate 62 (× 300). It has been established that these are convex hillocks surrounded by shallow trenches which outline the network.

One of the most remarkable features we have observed on several good quality dodecahedra is the frequent appearance of circular markings of the type shown in Plate 63 (× 100). An interferogram of this, Plate 64 (× 100), can be interpreted as follows. The surface as a whole, like most dodecahedral surfaces, is cylindrically curved. The circular region is an elevated disc, some 1700 Å in height and there is evidence of etch pits on the surface. Over a thousand such features have been recorded by us. We believe that the diamond, in its final stages, has had a mobile bubble of liquid or gas in contact with it at the position of the circle. The dodecahedron surface in its final stages has suffered solution ; the etch pits and the network patterns prove this. However, the bubble, whatever its nature, has had a protective action, preventing re-solution. Thus it is that the region of contact remains elevated whilst the rest of the surface is slightly dissolved away. The multiplicity of rings tied together (sometimes as many as twenty seem to originate from one diametral region) can easily be explained by postulating slight oscillations of the bubble to different, but very near-by, positions.

It seems very difficult to account for such circular patterns on diamond in terms of growth mechanisms. Whether this explanation is correct or not, the correct identification of the rings as elevated discs is of course only to be attributed to the use of interferometry.

REFERENCES

Nos. 11, 18, 39, 47, 49, 51, F, K, Q.

7. QUARTZ CRYSTALS

Natural—Synthetic—References.

Natural Quartz Crystals

THE ubiquitous mineral, quartz, lends itself to endless examination by multiple-beam interferometry. It can be obtained in large perfect single crystals with faces of high optical quality and is a material which has repaid the considerable study devoted to it interferometrically. Quartz is found both right- and left-handed and is typically a six-sided prism, terminating with major (R) and minor (r) rhombohedral faces as illustrated in Fig. 28. The long prism faces are usually striated and not very well suited to precision examination. On the other hand the R and r faces yield much of interest.

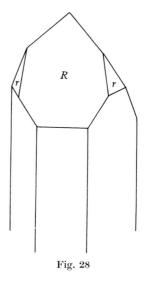

Fig. 28

It has been established that these faces are never plane, but always enclose vicinal faces, usually of slight cylindrical curvature. Plate 65 (× 15) shows detail on a typical R face, such triangular pyramidal centres being often seen. Each pyramid is a vicinal peak region and the faces are separated by straight edges, ridges, which interferometry shows are such that the slope on each side varies gradually. Fringes for this region are shown in Plate 66 (× 12) at slightly lower magnification. Notable is the high optical quality of the surface. Striations must be very shallow indeed. It is seen that the angle between fringes gradually changes along the r ridge-line running diagonally *up* from the middle left side of the picture. This interferogram is instructive. It is arranged in what has been called the ' geographical ' dispersion so that the fringes are running round the striated markings of Plate 65. Each fringe appears at its appropriate height and owing to the narrowness of the intensity distribution, nothing is seen between the fringes and the character there is missed. This is a feature which must always be watched for and the remedy is simple,

83

65

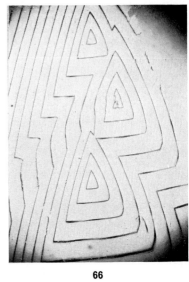

66

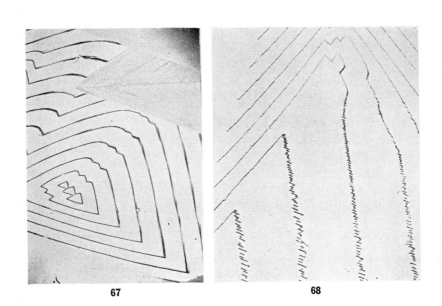

67

68

Plates 65-68

for it is only necessary to select fringes dispersed in a direction to *cross* the striae instead of being parallel with them in order to reveal the character of the striations.

This is shown to particular advantage by the following two examples which refer to a region on the same crystal as that shown by Plate 65. Plate 67 (× 25) is an R face which has on it three nearby growth centres which indicate the existence of a series of striation steps, and here the dispersion is almost geographic. In fact careful attention to the fringes shows that they are not quite parallel to the underlying striae and are disjointed therefrom. Now consider the appearance on such a striated region when dispersion is arranged such that the fringes *cross* the striae

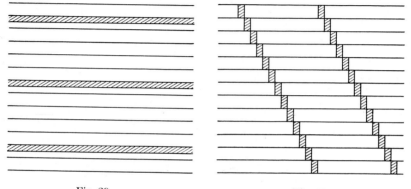

Fig. 29   Fig. 30

as in Plate 68 (× 25), which is for a neighbouring region on the same surface as that of Plate 67. This is a striking picture revealing at once the whole character of the striated surface. The possibility of over-looking shallow stepped striations is a practical point of considerable importance and it is re-emphasized schematically by Fig. 29 and Fig. 30. In Fig. 29 are shown diagrammatically a succession of fringes on a striated step-like surface (fringes are broad lines, steps are narrow lines) in which the dispersion is such that the fringes are *parallel* to the steps. With this arrangement the fringes *give no indication at all* of the existence of the steps, and one cannot distinguish between this staircase and an almost plane surface. But if the fringe dispersion is such that the fringes run *perpendicularly* to the steps then this leads to the situation of Fig. 30. The step pattern is now fully revealed. The conclusion is evident ; one must always take at least two interferograms in general, with dispersions more or less at right angles, a point already emphasized before but re-emphasized once more here.

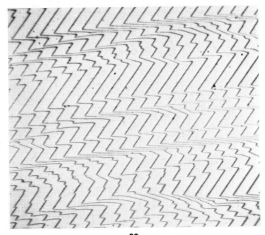

69

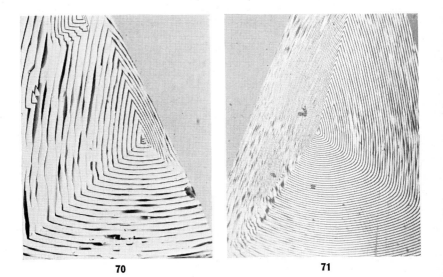

70   71

Plates 69-71

72

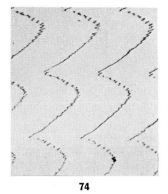

74

73

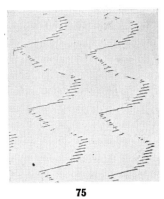

75

Plates 72-75

In general this condition is invariably satisfied during visual examination with fringes. For as the adjusting screws are moved the fringe pattern usually sweeps round, and as each screw is moved in turn one has dispersions going round full circle. Which particular dispersion is to be used for photography is a matter for selection, adapted in accordance with the nature of the surface under study.

At this point attention is again drawn to the fact that *this admirable showing-up of small-scale fine structure by the fringes is only possible with a correct optical technique.* Inexpert experimenters who have tried the multiple-beam method have frequently lost this detail. A principal reason is probably that of having too great a separation which leads to confusion of beams and failure to secure local contouring of detail.

A frequent condition appearing on R faces is that in which these shallow growth sheets bunch together and cause periodicity. A typical example of such periodic bunching is shown interferometrically in Plate 69 (× 40).

The growth fronts on the minor rhombohedral r faces resemble those on the R faces but an interesting difference in symmetry appears respectively in the right- and left-hand crystals. Thus Plate 70 (× 35) shows the topography of the r face on a *right*-handed crystal, and by comparison Plate 71 (× 35) shows that on a *left*-handed crystal. The hand is detectable from the direction of the vicinal edge running from the summit of the central pyramid which the fringe pattern shows up so clearly.

One other feature on r faces calls for comment. Plate 72 (× 40) is a relatively perfect case of an r face. It shows kinking in the growth front along the vicinal edges. Occasionally bunching appears on r faces as well as on R faces and one of the most striking interpretations of such bunching is shown by the following plates.

The actual face is shown in Plate 73 (× 40) and it is recognizable that at the top is a small pyramid formed by the meeting of vicinal faces. From this, a succession of waves of growth sheets has spread down. Fringes (at somewhat increased magnification) are shown in Plate 74 (× 50) and Plate 75 (× 50). Plate 74 refers to the region of widespread bunching, near the summit, whilst Plate 75 refers to a region lower down, away from the summit. In Plate 74 the individual growth secondary fronts, which pile up to form the bunches, are less than 100 Å high. But further away from the summit, in Plate 75, the growth fronts are some 200 Å high. These beautiful pictures show up well the mechanism of the bunching process.

Synthetic Quartz Crystals

The growth of large fine-quality synthetic quartz crystals from solution at high pressures has now become an industrial operation, the crystals being required for piezo-electric control of electronic circuits. We were engaged on a study of the topographies of some of these crystals prepared in the early stages of the evolution of a successful growth technique. The earlier crystals were much less perfect that those now made. Some experiments were carried out with a view to observing how growth initiated in the early stages. A seed crystal was cut parallel to a major rhombohedral R face and then fine-ground. A small amount of growth was deposited on this and the seed then examined by interferometry. The result obtained is shown by Plate 76 (× 30). It is seen that growth has initiated at several independent local regions in the form of flat pyramids, more or less of the same height. The main surface fringes are rough because of the original rough surface finish of the seed. Careful inspection shows a widespread distribution of small shallow etch pits, which were doubtless formed during the cooling-down process when growth had ceased. At a later stage pyramids develop more extensively over the whole surface. After a thickness growth of 1·5 microns the topography becomes that of Plate 77 (× 30) and here there is a resemblance to a rather poor type of natural surface of quartz.

However, crystals are now being produced in which selected perfect examples have surfaces almost devoid of any irregular structure apart from local curvature. On some examples of these we have discovered some peculiar unique growth features which we have failed to explain as yet. The synthetic r surfaces on our crystals are very flat and smooth, but locally there appear strange shapes which are strictly oriented. These appear on a large r face of a synthetic crystal grown by G.E.C. on a seed plate, which was rectangular, of dimensions $5 \times 3\frac{1}{2}$ cm. The crystal was grown from a solution maintained at 350° C and under a pressure of 1000 atmospheres. Rate of growth was about 0·5 mm in thickness per day.

An interferogram of part of this surface is shown in Plate 78 (× 35). When this is compared with the natural r faces it is seen to differ very markedly. The surface is quite free from the usual natural pyramid structure. The fringes are, it is true, less smooth than those given by a really good natural crystal, but apart from local features the surface is a good one.

There are some very remarkable features on this surface and two of these are shown (phase-contrast microscope), in Plate 79 (× 150). The

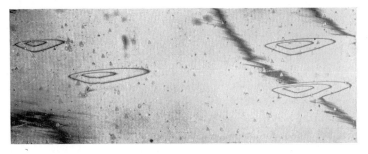

76

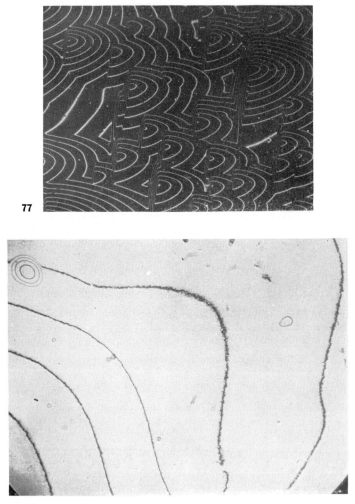

77

78

Plates 76-78

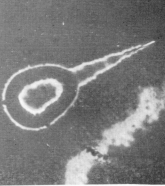

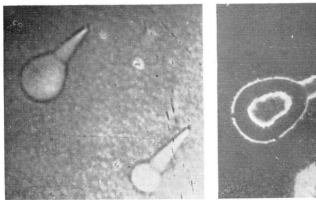

79

80

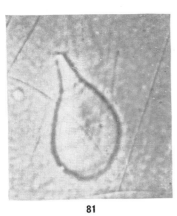

81

82

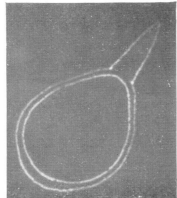

83

Plates 79-83

G 2

fringe pattern for one of these peculiarly shaped features is shown in Plate 80 ($\times$ 250). Another such feature is shown in Plate 81 ($\times$ 170) and the interferogram for this in Plate 82 ($\times$ 170). A fringe pattern for another at higher magnification is shown in Plate 83 ($\times$ 350). These features are all elevations, the rounded ' body ' being usually about two fringes in height and the ' tail ' always less. The bodies are all oriented and seem to point along the c-axis of the crystal. It seems plausible to regard these possibly as overgrowths, possibly as liquid or gaseous inclusions. Many features are curious, such as the dark band where the ' tail ' joins the ' body '.

It will be noticed in Plate 81 that the main feature has a very faint elongated region near the ' tail '. This is shown up as a deep, dark shadow region in Plate 82, where a broad, fairly highly dispersed fringe passes just over this feature. Its height, although unknown from this picture, is much less than half a light wave. This shows well that interferometric contrast is much more vivid than the phase contrast.

REFERENCES

Nos. 4, 6, 41.

8. SOME CRYSTAL GROWTHS

Silicon carbide spirals—Spirals on chrysene—Germanium dendrites —Haematite—References.

Studies of Spiral Growths on Silicon Carbide

SOME extensive studies have been made in my laboratory on growth spirals on silicon carbide crystals. Many hundreds of micrographs and interferograms have been obtained and a good deal of information secured on the mechanism of spiral growth. All the diverse evidence strongly supports the Franck theory of spiral growth. Since Verma, in his book *Crystal Growth and Dislocations* (Butterworth, 1953), has gone into much detail concerning this application of interferometry to silicon carbide crystals, the aim here will be only to consider (*a*) the application of interferometry to the subject of spiral growth, and (*b*) the converse exploitation of crystal spirals in connection with interferometric practice. The first supporting evidence for Franck's theory of crystal growth by a spiral dislocation mechanism was obtained in my laboratory by Griffin in 1951, who found such a spiral on beryl and succeeded by multiple-beam interferometry in estimating the step height as $8 \cdot 5$ Å ± 1 Å. Considering the difficulty involved in this particular observation it can be taken that this is identical with the $7 \cdot 9$ Å repeat distance on (1010) given by X-rays, which is the step value expected. The difference, a mere $0 \cdot 6$ Å, has no real significance. From then on, intensive work has been pursued in studying spirals with multiple-beam interferometry. In particular, Verma, Bhide and Amelinckx have achieved much of value by this approach. Observed spirals on silicon carbide can be classed into many varieties, regular-elementary, disso-ciated, compound, multiple, closed-loop, interlaced, etc. Silicon carbide exists in a variety of polytypes, in all of which the crystal lattice spacings differ. In these, in the hexagonal cell, the a_0 spacing is always $3 \cdot 07$ Å but the different polytypes have c_0 spacings which are distinctive in that the number of layers is different. Several different notations to describe the polytypes have been proposed, that of Ramsdell being adopted here (given in brackets). The different polytypes have respec-tive c_0 spacings, in ångströms, equal to $10 \cdot 05(4H)$, $15 \cdot 08(6H)$, $37 \cdot 70(15R)$, $52 \cdot 78(21R)$, $82 \cdot 94(33R)$ and $128 \cdot 18(51R)$. In the Ramsdell notation the number indicates the number of layers and the letter refers to the hexagonal (H) or the rhombohedral (R) cell.

Consider first the beautiful growth spiral shown in Plate 84 (× 300). Phase contrast microscopy has been used. The spiral starts off from a black dot (dislocation axis) and begins in a curved way, but quickly converts into a rectilinear hexagonal pattern with rounded corners.

A multiple-beam interferogram at appreciably lower magnification over the peak of this spiral is shown in Plate 85 (× 66). This is full of interesting information. The spiral is seen to consist of a beautifully regular staircase and the fringes have been arranged to pass almost over the peak. The steps are remarkably uniform in height and measure 165 Å, the mean averaged error being ± 1 Å. Two other features are of interest : (a) because the spiral winds, an overall curvature appears on the fringe running over the spiral ; and (b) the fringes are remarkably true and uniform on the spiral staircase ' treads '. This is seen not only on the separate step-like fringes, but especially on the fringes at the top of the picture which happen to be along the staircase in such a direction as to run more or less parallel to the spiral edge. This leads to a long remarkable uniform fringe section. It seems clear that the spiral faces are molecular planes. Succeeding interferograms will amply substantiate this conjecture.

Now it so happens that most of the spirals have been found on the 6H variety of silicon carbide on the basal plane (0001) which has 15·08 Å as the c-lattice parameter and on this it has been established with some degree of certainty that the observed staircase height is an *exact single lattice* spacing. One way in which this has been done is illustrated by the fringe pattern shown in Plate 86 (× 110). Two high-dispersion fringes are shown. The one passing over the peak of the spiral shows this as a hill-top, the height of which can be measured directly. The spiral turns can be clearly seen, but each step is hardly resolved. Yet it is easy to count the number of steps on the hill and, by dividing this into the height of the hill, Verma obtained 15·2 Å as an average, with an error of ± 1 Å. This step height is a mere 0·12 Å more than the X-ray lattice parameter and this certainly establishes that the spiral is exactly *one* lattice in height. *The evaluation of such lattice spacings by optical interferometry is a considerable optical achievement.* In the 15R and 33R polytypes spirals have been found with step height equal to the rhombohedral cell length a_{rh} which is one third of the c_0 spacing. These steps have been closely identified with the theoretical values.

With Bhide we have derived the step height on a 6R spiral by exploiting geographical dispersion, the optical flat being set tangential to the

84

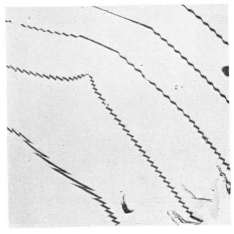

85

Plates 84, 85

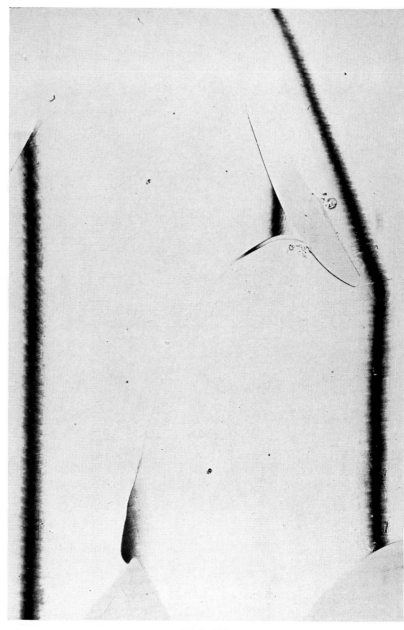

Plate 86

spiral peak. This is an elegant method and is illustrated as follows. Plate 87 (× 220) shows the spiral in question and it is close-packed, the spiral arms being near to each other. A fringe system at ' geographical ' dispersion is shown in Plate 88 (× 22), i.e. at only a tenth of the magnification. Two fringes appear, one fairly near the peak, the other a good distance away. They are separated by 2730 Å in height (green mercury light). A count can be made of the number of spiral turns between these two fringes. There is some uncertainty partly because of fringe width, partly in the character of the spiral. The number found is about 190. Dividing gives 14·4 Å for the step height which is sufficiently close to the lattice spacing 15·08 Å.

Now when the fringe dispersion is altered to be similar to that of the Plate 86, the fringe pattern secured for the spiral of Plate 87 is that shown in Plate 89 (× 35). The single steps are not resolved but what is shown vividly is the non-linear character of the spiral. The hill has concave sides and the slope progressively increases on approaching the dislocation, which is at the centre of the hillock. The curvature is easily computed from Plate 89. The reason for this curvature is evident. If the arms are exactly equally spaced by an amount d (here of the order of 5·25 micron) then the unresolved spiral fringes will rise in a linear conical fashion with slope h/d where h is the step height. Substitution gives the angle $2·85 \times 10^{-4}$ radian. Now the measures of the slope obtained from Plate 89 are as follows. At a distance of 280μ from the centre, the slope is $3·4 \times 10^{-4}$ radian, at 120μ it has increased to $5·1 \times 10^{-4}$ radian and near the peak itself it rises still further to $6·2 \times 10^{-4}$ radian. The reason can be seen in Plate 87. The successive loops are in fact getting slowly further apart as the spiral develops, thus d is gradually increasing. This explains the shape of the fringe pattern. The *height* remains a *strict lattice spacing*, but the stair width increases, hence the slope of the cone changes.

With a Vickers E.M.3 electron microscope we have studied further some of the spirals already examined by interferometry. We have long considered that whilst Formvar replication in *extension* is effectively perfect, replication in *depth* can be suspect. We have therefore examined the crystals (a) by direct reflection electron microscopy which avoids any replication, and (b) Formvar and carbon replication. In reflection electron microscopy the electron beam strikes at a glancing incidence and this leads to extreme foreshortening of the picture in the direction of viewing, and a highly localized focus. The foreshortened picture of a spiral edge, at × 6000 is shown in Plate 90. This is a crystal with step height 180 Å. The step edge appears to be single. A Formvar-carbon

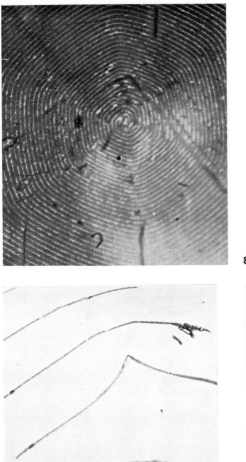

87

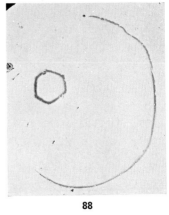

88

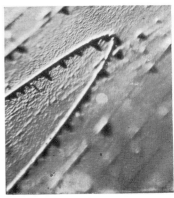

90

89

91

Plates 87-91

replica, shadow-cast with gold, at the very high magnification of 45,000 times gave the step edge shown in Plate 91. On this scale of magnification it is quite clear that the steps are (a) single, and (b) frequently kinked.

On some very high definition interferograms on SiC spirals there is clear evidence of a slip near the centre of the spiral. Plate 92 (× 120) shows an interferogram over a spiral in which the fringe near the spiral centre has a distinct kink in it. This spiral has a chain of circular pits running on its edges (possibly etch) and so the spiral shape is well delineated. The slip of the fringe pattern is very clearly shown here.

A remarkable fringe picture of a slip effect which spreads for some distance in a conical fashion is shown by the interferogram Plate 93 (× 60). The fringe definition here is superb. Towards the top left is a fringe kink, which can be interpreted as a slip step due to a cone source. The step height itself on this remarkable interferogram is 480 Å and the slip step is of exactly identical value showing that the whole dislocation has moved.

Between two radial arms inclined at 30° and leaving the centre it is clear that the crystal surface is not flat, but kinked. Plate 94 (× 130) shows fringes of equal chromatic order which cross this region and show the kink to advantage. Plate 95 (× 130) shows similar fringes illustrating the kink and also reaching and crossing a step of the spiral.

Another phenomenon arising from pairs of dislocations, which is quite common, is the formation of a channel running along a spiral. The micrograph Plate 96 (× 70) shows part of a large spiral in which there appears to be what resembles a broad channel. The correct interpretation is shown by Plate 97 (× 70) which shows the fringes of equal chromatic order across a selected region of the spiral. The picture is turned through 90° to show the direction of the profile relative to Plate 96. The value of the step on the spiral itself is 168 Å and the channel is almost exactly four times this (coming down from the higher side, but three times from the lower side). All this information is of considerable crystallographic interest, but this will not be pursued here.

One feature emerges from these interferograms which turns out to be of value. This is that it is clear that *between the spiral arms the surface is crystallographically perfect.* We have the rare phenomenon of a true crystallographically perfect surface which is not plane, in the sense of being absolutely flat, since the spiral winds up, but is in section effectively straight. Here is the perfect step edge for study, for adjacent regions separated by a spiral turn are ideally suited as a base for step studies. This fact we have fully exploited. The quality and straightness of the

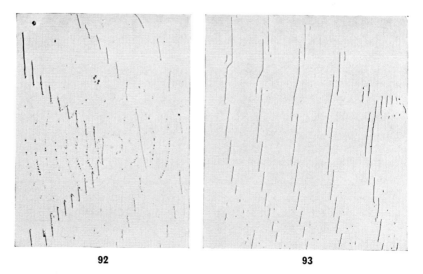

92   93

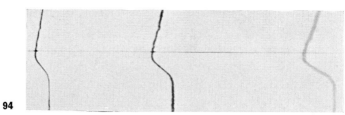

94

95

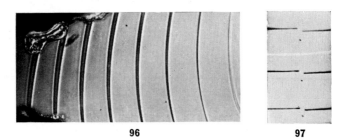

96   97

Plates 92-97

fringes indicate that silicon carbide offers perfect surfaces for use in studying properties of thin films.

Spirals on Chrysene

At this point attention can be drawn to the very marked difference between the information offered by multiple-beam and by two-beam systems. The fringe definition in multiple-beam systems is far superior to that in the two-beam variety, but one point of value in connection with two-beam interferometry is the relative ease of obtaining the fringes even with very high lateral magnifications. In multiple-beams, very high lateral magnifications require most critical illumination conditions. The two-beam fringes will be considered in relation to spiral growth observed on some thin organic crystal plates. Their use is by no means to be despised. We have made a study of spiral growth phenomena in some hydro-carbon aromatics and these include thin, rhomb-shaped, crystals of chrysene, grown from xylene solution. These grow in very thin plates with flat or stepped areas on the one side and often with a well-developed spiral on the other side. The scale is usually small. Plate 98 ($\times$ 900) shows with quite a high magnification a doubly inter-laced spiral system. There is much complexity ; for instance the dark line running right towards the middle bottom from near the spiral centre seems to refer to the back surface, as the spiral arms are not affected by it. On the other hand the line at right angles to this going up to the top middle suggests that the crystals flake has here bent and twisted.

By illuminating in parallel monochromatic light, two-beam fringes can be obtained *within* the crystal itself, as shown in Plate 99 ($\times$ 1100). These confirm that the lower line is due to a growth sheet change on the *rear* surface. This is a situation similar to that of the multiple-beam picture of Plate 88 but the fringe width here leads to considerable uncertainty. There are perhaps ten turns between fringes, but clearly the uncertainty extends over a number of turns. The step height (taking refractive index into account) approximates to some 200 Å, but this is uncertain to within possibly 30 Å or more. Another typical example is shown in Plate 100 ($\times$ 550). Here the uncertainty is considerable. There are five turns between fringes, but within any one turn the system is so insensitive as to lead to uniform tint within the *whole* turn, despite the fact that the step must be of the order of 400 Å. Similar difficulty and uncertainty is shown in Plate 101 ($\times$ 550) for another spiral.

The accuracy is clearly of a lower order than for a multiple-beam sys-tem, which, with a similar approach has yielded steps correct to within a fraction of a single ångström unit.

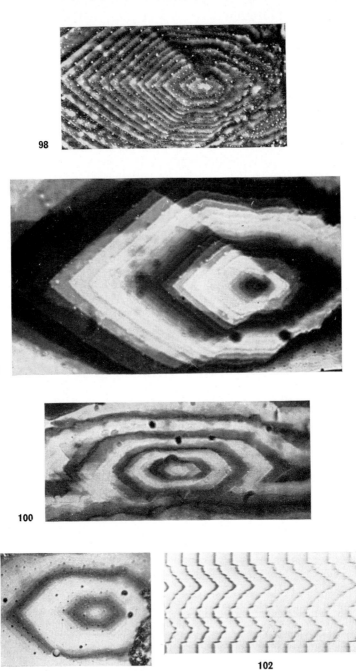

98

99

100

101

102

Plates 98-102

We have succeeded in silvering the spiral faces of a chrysene crystal and thus obtained multiple-beam fringes of equal chromatic order. Plate 102 (× 90) is an example which has two adjacent spirals on it. These show that the spirals are complex, the larger having on it steps of 437 and 328 Å respectively, information quite unobtainable by the two-beam method. Definition is not very good compared with that obtained on silicon-carbide spirals.

A Feature on Germanium Dendrites

It is familiarly known that many metals when rapidly crystallized appear in dendritic form. Germanium grows readily in such dendrites. E. Billig has supplied us with crystals of pure germanium, grown from the melt and seeded to produce a flat long dendritic plate with faces and edges crystallographically oriented, the main face belonging to the $\{111\}$ family of planes. The crystals bear a relation to the flat portrait stones found amongst diamonds. The long, flat-plate, dendritic crystal has a central ' backbone ' and when examined by a microscope, Plate 103 (× 70), this is seen to consist of a series of triangular patterns linked to form a straight line. The spacing between the triangular features is variable, although the sizes of the triangles are not too dissimilar. They are all equilateral and the boundary edges lie along $\langle \bar{1}10 \rangle$, the vertices pointing towards $\langle 11\bar{2} \rangle$.

The curious character of these chains of triangles is to some extent revealed by multiple-beam interferometry. Fringes of equal chromatic order over four typical triangular features are shown in Plate 104 (× 70). The fringes are turned through 90° to follow the contour of Plate 103. They are found to vary in height from some 200 Å to 300 Å and are clearly shallow pyramids. The high interferometric vertical magnification must not be allowed to confuse the position. The slopes of the inclined faces vary from some three to nine *minutes* of arc. They are shallow vicinal faces, deviating slightly from (111).

Haematite

Haematite is a crystal which grows often with a beautiful natural glance, and some systematic studies on samples from Japan have been made in my laboratory by I. Sunagawa. Some of the surfaces are highly complex and reveal multiple-spiral growths. Sunagawa has succeeded in measuring the height of a very shallow spiral with 30 clearly marked turns in it. From the height of this he has obtained the remarkably small value of 2·3 Å for the step height per turn. This is precisely the X-ray lattice distance, and is the *smallest step yet evaluated by any*

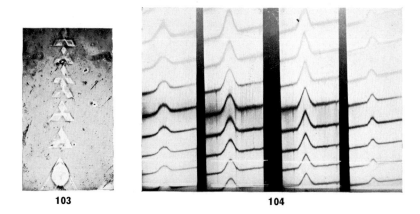

103   **104**

interferometric procedure. Unfortunately the observable contrast in this spiral is such as to defeat reproduction in this text. Yet the way in which remarkable interferometric definition has been achieved with this crystal can be illustrated on some of the larger steps, steps which are still very small.

Plate 105 ($\times$ 90) is a composite, built up from microphotographs of one particular region on the haematite crystal. This photograph has been secured with an extremely effective Japanese Olympus phase-contrast microscope. The particular objective used has an extremely absorbing phase disc (increasing exposure time by a factor of 400) and this enables very shallow step edges to be brought up into relatively strong contrast.

The picture shows a well-marked oval feature at the top and below it are three clearly defined growth ledges, one near the oval, two lower down, running diagonally from left to right, upwards. As is usual in phase-contrast pictures, the dark edge is lined with a spurious white diffraction edge.

An interferogram of this region is shown in Plate 106 ($\times$ 90), from which it is seen that the oval disc is at a quite different level from the rest of the surface.

The first point to which attention is drawn is the excellence of the fringe definition. The fringes are spaced about 43 mm apart and the fringe width does not exceed 40 Å. When the fringe pattern of Plate 106 is compared with the micrograph of Plate 105 the displaced step in the fringes as they pass over the growth edges is clearly seen. *Measurement shows these edges are only 30 Å in height* and yet this is quite clearly easily resolved. Indeed on the original of Plate 105 can be seen the

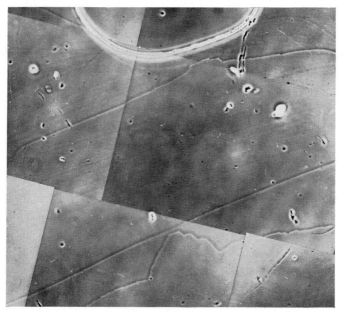

105

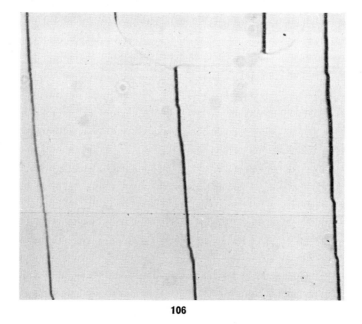

106

Plates 105, 106

beginning of a series of very faint growth edges, about 1 cm below the first main edge under the oval disc and on all fringes a kink at this edge is clearly observable. It is fairly certain that a step of 5 Å could be detected. This appears to be near the ultimate limit in this type of multiple-beam interferometry. The derivation of the value 2·3 Å mentioned above is obtained from an unresolved multiple set of steps.

It is, however, well to realize that whilst this 5 Å is at present the limit for a direct numerical measurement, even higher sensitivity is possible when high dispersion colour tint methods are used. Changes in level of only 3 Å can then cause a detectable change in colour. As yet no attempt has been made to exploit colour tints as a basis for numerical evaluation of step height since colour tints are notoriously difficult to assess visually, and as yet defy an easy instrumental assessment.

REFERENCES

No. 50, T.

9. ETCHED DIAMONDS

The etching of diamond—Octahedral faces—Dodecahedral faces—Cubic faces—References.

The Etching of Diamond

EXTENSIVE studies we have made over several years on the etching of a variety of diamond faces have yielded results of crystallographic interest and, as these investigations have been uniformly concurrently assisted by interferometric studies, a summary of the findings is included here, largely because the two techniques, etching and interferometry, have consistently helped and supported each other, and have formed together a very powerful combination.

Although even Robert Boyle declared in the seventeenth century that a diamond ' dissipates into acrid vapours ' when strongly heated, and whilst Lavoisier proved that it burned away to CO_2, the study of diamond etch has, until we took it up, been much neglected. Rose in 1872 discussed natural etch figures on diamond, but it was Luzi in 1892 who conducted the first etch experiments by heating diamonds in their native ' blue ground ' ore, kimberlite, at over 1700° C. The diamonds were, he reported, largely eaten away. The etch was clearly too fierce to be of much value. Fersmann and Goldschmidt in their classic work on diamond (1911) produced triangular etch pits on octahedra and on cleavages by heating for some hours in KNO_3 at 900° C and Williams, under identical conditions, reported on some etch experiments on octahedron, dodecahedron and cubic faces.

We have found that the slow *controlled* etch which is desirable for studying etch phenomena starts at a reasonable rate on diamond at about 525° when it is immersed in fresh KNO_3. Etching for about 1 hour suffices to produce an adequate pattern. At even 650° the whole surface is quickly attacked on a micro-scale. It is imperative in these experiments to use a *slow* controlled etch, for only under such conditions does the etch preferentially attack a variety of features of crystallographic interest. By doing so it develops up patterns which are of much value in connection with crystal studies. If the etch is allowed to run too rapidly then the very surface features being sought for are destroyed. We have etched natural octahedron faces, polished dodecahedral planes, cubic planes, and cleavages. The study of the cleavages has proved the more exciting, but a brief general survey of the work we have done will be given in what follows.

Octahedron Faces

Diamond octahedron faces usually show the shallow trigons already described, with their familiar orientation. When such a face is etched, triangular etch pits appear and these are *always oriented oppositely to the trigons*. The side edges of the trigons themselves are also attacked. The etch pits at the beginning of the action are very small and widely distributed as shown in Plate 107 (× 200) which shows early-stage etch surrounding a typical trigon. The trigon sides have been themselves attacked also. The pits are rectilinear and have flat bottoms. The shape, both in outline and in depth, of the etch pits depends upon the rate of etch and time of exposure to etchant. There is a regular evolution, but it is convenient to divide the etch into three arbitrary stages. In the first stage isolated pits appear, as many as at least some 2×10^7 per sq cm being resolvable in some regions. In the second stage no *new* pits appear but those already there grow, become rounded and encroach into each other, the larger ultimately devouring the smaller. In the third stage, when the whole original surface has been eaten away, a striking block pattern emerges, accompanied by deep, flat-bottom, large, shapeless craters.

Although etch normally begins at about 500° C it is possible to induce a *very slow* etch rate at 475° and Plate 108 (× 800) shows the pattern secured after 42 hours of exposure to the etchant at this temperature. The pits are small and quite rectilinear. If now the surface is exposed at a mere 50° more (525° C) then etching begins to develop rapidly and in only $1\frac{1}{2}$ hours the pattern on Plate 109 (× 800) appears. The pits are growing and deepening and corners are rounding. In another $1\frac{1}{2}$ hours, at still the same temperature, Plate 110 (× 800) is secured. Rounding is more marked and pits have begun to eat each other up. Some are flat-bottomed, others have a pyramidal point apex, or tend to this. What is notable is that original pits grow but virtually no new pits appear, other than very shallow small pits *within* existing large pits.

At a very advanced stage of etching single pits become large craters, eating up the surrounding area and showing masses of secondary shallow pits on the flat base as can be seen in Plate 110.

At a higher temperature, say 650° C, the tendency is for deep pointed pits to evolve, Plate 111 (× 130) illustrates an interferogram which shows the topographies of such pits. There is much rounding and some

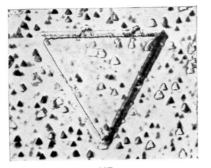

107

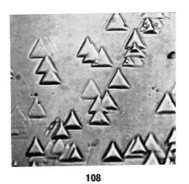

108

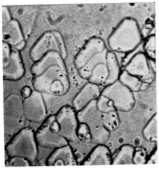

109

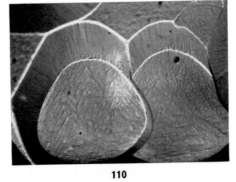

110

111

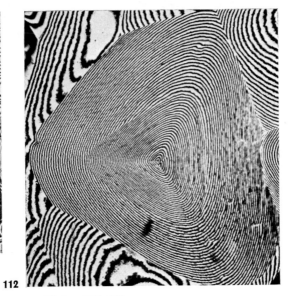

112

Plates 107-112

113

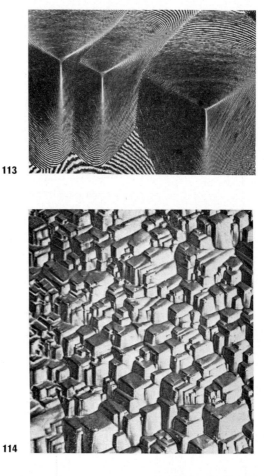

114

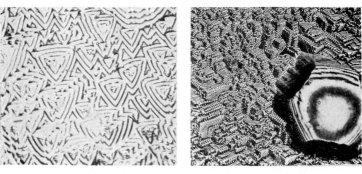

115   116

Plates 113-116

pits have flat bottoms, others are pointed. An examination can be made of both shallow and deep pits by interferometry. Plate 112 ($\times$ 250) is a very deep pit examined this way. The depth of this is considerable, almost 1/50th mm and the sides drop in at an angle of 10° off the horizontal. The fringes show that the apex is double, a detail hardly detectable without interferometry.

A continuation of this mechanism can in some cases lead to the evolution of a remarkable block pattern. A stage in this evolution is shown by the interferogram Plate 113 ($\times$ 200) which shows such a coarse block pattern emerging. By this stage appreciable crystal dissolution has taken place and the pits have converted themselves into pyramidal *depressions*. The deepest here is about a hundred fringes deep, i.e. 0·027 mm. The sides have a slight but unmistakable curvature, since the dispersion is not quite linear. The sides slope in at some 10°.

One particular crystal, after two hours at 650° C, produced a most striking block pattern. A section of this is shown in Plate 114 ($\times$ 800). These regular blocks do not have 90° corners, as is established by the interferogram Plate 115 ($\times$ 700). This was taken with the 3-mm objective corrected for cover slip thickness. The sides of the blocks are mainly (221), (122), (212) planes as established by the interference fringes. In addition (331) and (313) appear. Always associated with the microblock patterns, of which quite a number have now been produced on different crystals, are deep craters with very flat bottoms. Plate 116 ($\times$ 270) shows an interferogram over a region containing blocks and one deep crater. The uniformity at the base of the crater is noteworthy. Some such craters have diameter of 0·1 mm and depth of some 4μ and it is apparent that the etch preferentially spreads *sideways*, not downwards. This would suggest that the base of the crater is a good crystallographic region free from dislocations.

The Dodecahedron Plane

When the etch experiments were first being carried out no dodecahedron diamond was available with good enough dodecahedral faces for interferometric study. The majority of the faces even on the best of dodecahedra are either striated, rough, or exhibit a complex network. Therefore an octahedral diamond was sawn and polished to a close approximation to the dodecahedral crystallographic direction. This surface was then etched.

A one-hour etch at 550° C produced an enormous number of micropits which were arranged in a remarkable and unexpected pattern. Plate 117 ($\times$ 20) shows the whole crystal face. Originally smooth and

117

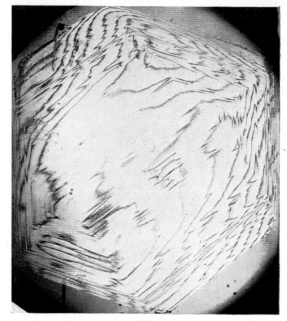

118
Plates 117, 118

119

120

121

Plates 119-121

fairly plane, the etching has produced a concentric linear pattern. The individual pits are hardly resolvable with a microscope.

An interferogram is illustrated in Plate 118 (× 20) from which it can be inferred that the central region is still fairly flat, but is now surrounded by concentric descending staircase-like sheets.

When the etching is continued further, separate individual oriented boat-shaped small pits appear. These are of interest crystallographically but will not be discussed here in that interferometry has not been applied in detail to these features.

The explanation of the striking hexagonal array of pits is as follows. When sectioning the crystal, to produce the dodecahedral face, one cuts through all the former (111) faces which were laid down successively when the crystal grew. It is evident that the etch seeks out and attacks boundaries between successive layers. One can truly say that the etch is so sensitive that it has revealed the real *stratigraphy*, the history of the growth of the diamond. It would appear that a sheet can grow with crystallographic perfection. Then another may grow on this with imperfect continuity. The cut plane through the crystal sections these growth layers and although nothing of their character was at all visible on the original polished diamond, as soon as etch begins there is pre-ferential attack at the imperfect boundaries. Indeed where a thin layer of perfect crystal is laid down there is no attack, because of absence of imperfections, and such a perfect region or layer stands up proud as a ridge. Many such ridges have been revealed interferometrically. It is seen here how both etch and interferometry support each other. When one recalls the very great sensitivity of multiple-beam interferometry to surface markings it is important to realize that etching must by inference be sensitive to markings and depressions of *the order of a single lattice spacing or even less*, for the etch is showing up patterns which are not even hinted at by interferometry. An important crystallographic conclusion from these studies is that they establish the layer growth formation of diamond. This would seem to weaken those theories which propose that a diamond crystallizes from a drop of molten carbon, i.e. grows from the melt.

Cubic Faces

On diamond, natural cubic faces are rare and usually very rough and totally unsuited to precision optical work. We therefore, as with the dodecahedron plane, also polished cube faces on diamonds. The polish secured was adequate, as instanced by Plate 119 (× 20). Etching was less rapid than with the dodecahedral face, but once again two types of etch were found, (*a*) a concentric rectangular linear pattern, enclosing vast numbers of unresolved pits, and separate individual square pits. Plate 120 ($\times$ 20) is an interferogram over the whole face. It shows three features : (*a*) again a succession of descending staircases ; (*b*) the fringes are broadened because of the multitude of minute pits ; and (*c*) many individual deep pits which are square-shaped, but rounded.

The rectilinear character is shown by Plate 121 ($\times$ 140). Three features emerge : (*a*) there is a dense region in which there are at least 2×10^6 pits per square millimetre ; (*b*) separate individual appreciably larger square pits appear ; and (*c*) there are regions entirely free from attack, presumably resistant because of being free from dislocations.

Once more the explanation of the rectilinear pattern is the same, the etching is revealing the strata laid down in (111) planes, and the cubic plane produced by sectioning shows the whole stratigraphy because of the differential attack of the etchant.

REFERENCES

Nos. 42, 43, 47, O, Q, Z.

PART THREE

SPECIAL TECHNIQUES

10. SPECIAL TECHNIQUES

Micro-flats—Overlaid thin films—The efficiency of thin-film contouring—Experimental study of contouring—Multilayer dielectric films—References.

Micro-flats

THE imposition of the desirable condition of very small separation between object and optical flat can often introduce difficulties in special cases. Frequently natural crystals are found with a raised edge, or a hillock, or an elevated region, which may project even several millimetres. This prevents close approach to the lower regions when an ordinary optical flat is used. This difficulty has been overcome in some cases by the employ of micro-flats. These are small truncated cones cut from a good selected piece of fire-polished glass, either from a flat or from a selected piece of thin glass sheet. Conveniently the cone tip can be of diameter 1 mm or less and the base may be some three times as big. The cone tip need not be polished if the cone be selected from a suitable piece of glass. It is mounted on the microscope, after silvering, with a simple centre adjusting device. Surprisingly good small local regions can be found on pieces of old photographic plate.

With a cone cut from a piece of selected photographic plate it is thin enough to enable an 8-mm objective to be employed and such micro-flats have found considerable employ with us. An admirable example of their use is shown in Plate 122 ($\times$ 200). Here is shown a series of alternative coarse and fine slip bands which have appeared on a titanium single crystal which has been subjected to shear forces. The crystal was large and very concave and an ordinary flat would have led to *very large* separations between the surfaces with consequent broadening and loss in detail too. The micro-cone was introduced deep into the concavity and permitted adequate close approach to near the pole of the concave surface. The concave character of the surface is shown by the fringe dispersion and the curvature is of the order of one or two centimetres. Considering the difficulty of such a surface the fringe definition is good and this is attributable largely to the micro-flat permitting reasonably close approach.

Overlaid Thin-Film Technique

We have often realized that the requirement of an optical flat can in some cases introduce limitations. Thus if high powers are to be employed, then only very short working distances are at disposal. The working distances available with 3 or 4 mm dry objectives of high numerical aperture restrict the optical flat to something very thin. Fortunately the very high power implies that the field of view is limited to much less than a square millimetre, indeed one is generally content to observe a disc of diameter 1/10th millimetre or even less, since at $\times$ 1000 such a disc gives an image of diameter 10 cm. It is this restriction in area which permits crude flats to be used and it need only be once more re-emphasized that a crude flat of 1 cm diameter, correct even to only one light wave, is then locally correct to $\lambda/100$ over the region under consideration *provided the surface is smooth*. As already pointed out, smooth finish becomes far more important than flatness when using high powers.

Our requirement becomes a reference body which is quite thin, has a surface reasonably flat, but most important is smooth locally. This requirement can at times be met by : (*a*) specially selected thin microscope cover slips ; (*b*) selected thin sheets of mica ; and (*c*) thin plastic films. The selection of a suitable microscope cover-slip is a matter of chance. Thin sheets of mica usually wrinkle and may have cleavage steps on them and it is then difficult to adjust dispersion, yet it must be recognized that selected mica can be molecularly true over extensive areas, indeed over some square centimetres. We have had a little, but not much, experience with thin collodion sheets, spread from solution on water and picked up by a wire circlet. Such plastic ' flats ' distort through the deviation of the wire circlet from a plane and whilst they are adequately thin and can accept silvering yet there is uncertainty about the smoothness and we have not employed such films in our work as yet.

Here will be described alternative types of thin film techniques which in a sense can be regarded as non-stripping replication methods. No optical flat is used. The crystal surface under study is covered with a thin film which, on its lower side which is that in contact with the crystal, contours the crystal, and on its upper side forms a convex curved but very smooth surface. The method can only be used to reveal discontinuity, such as spiral steps, dislocations, etch pit edges and so on. It introduces false curvatures but this is of no consequence if it is deliberately restricted to revealing and measuring sharp discontinuous

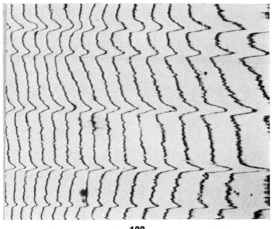

122

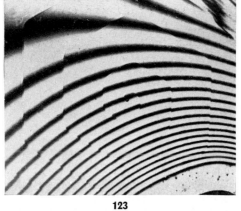

123

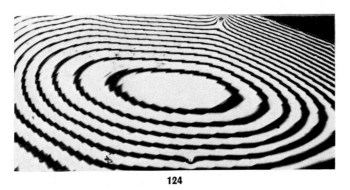

124

Plates 122-124

edges. A suitable film should fulfil at least three conditions : (a) it should faithfully contour steps and edges ; (b) it should be transparent ; and (c) it should be stable in a vacuum if it is to receive silver. We have found that either a dilute solution of Canada balsam in xylene or collodion in chloroform or ether fulfil these requirements.

The method can be used either with two interfering beams or with multiple-beams. With two-beams a droplet of the solution is run over the surface and allowed to drain off and dry. If viewed by a mercury-arc source, fringes can be seen moving over the surface as the liquid drains and dries off. By judiciously adjusting the direction of drain, a wedge film can be created with its wedge angle in any desired direction. The system after drying off is then examined in a high-power micro-scope with monochromatic light. It can only be viewed in reflection because of visibility considerations. Now two-beam fringe visibility under such an arrangement can be exceptionally good *when a high refractive index crystal* such as diamond or silicon carbide is under examination. Indeed the two-beam technique should be deliberately restricted to high index materials for the following reason. Let μ_1, μ_2, μ_3, be refractive indices of air, thin film and crystal. Then the air-film interface normal incidence reflectivity is $(\mu_2 - \mu_1)^2/(\mu_2 + \mu_1)^2$ and the film-crystal reflectivity is $(\mu_3 - \mu_2)^2/(\mu_3 + \mu_2)^2$. Perfect visi-bility obtains when these are equal and this condition leads to $\mu_1\mu_3 = \mu_2^2$, i.e. the same condition as obtains for anti-reflection bloom-ing. Taking μ_1 for air as unity and μ_2 for Canada balsam as 1·5 then the crystal index μ_3 should be 2·25. A diamond has refractive index close to this and silicon carbide is not very different (say 2·67). Hence we can expect with these high index crystals that the two-beam interference from reflections at the two faces of the film will give very good visibility since both reflected beams have the same intensity. This is the case.

As a first example is shown Plate 123 (× 270). Here is illustrated the thin film two-beam fringe pattern given near the centre of a growth spiral on a silicon carbide crystal. The following features are of interest. The broad fringes have extremely good contrast. In fact it was estab-lished, that apart from the flat spiral hillock the surface was fairly plane, but the fringes show an overall curvature which is spurious. However, the really significant feature is the way in which the step edges of the spiral are shown. These were measured here to be 210 ± 20 Å and it was established by precision multiple-beam interference that this was correct to within 10 Å.

That the inevitable distorting shape of the droplet need not seriously affect steps measurement is shown vividly by Plate 124 (× 200) for the same spiral, but here the region selected is far from the spiral centre and the true topography is masked by the convex droplet pattern which really belongs to the thin film. Yet the step height measured on this plate is 200 Å, close enough to the 210 Å established from the previous picture, despite the distortion due to the drop.

The limitations must naturally be strictly recognized. In Plate 125 (× 250) is shown a projecting end region on a crystal of SiC in which a spiral formation is ending. Alongside in Plate 126 (× 400) at higher magnification is the thin-film fringe pattern. There is exact correlation between the distinctive areas. Only the discontinuous step values are significant, the curvatures are falsities and must be disregarded, for a convex droplet has built up on the feature. Despite this, the step displacements can readily be evaluated to within the limitations of two-beam interferometry.

Some remarkably fine multiple-beam fringe definition at quite high magnifications can be obtained by combining silvering with the thin-film technique. This arises essentially because the film is so thin. An outstanding example is shown in Plate 127 (× 300). This interferogram refers to a diamond cleavage surface and magnification is fairly high (× 300). The cleaved diamond was first silvered and of course the silver contoured the cleavage lines. The thin film was next formed and this was then silvered. The fringes have remarkably fine definition for so high a magnification. The pattern is very deceiving for the diamond surface is certainly not curved as shown, it was actually in this instance nearly plane in this region (apart from cleavage steps). The only true topographical features which the technique reveals are the cleavage steps, which are beautifully and accurately delineated. The circular patterning is the false effect due to the convexity of the drop. If this false distortion is constantly borne in mind, it will be appreciated that some information of very real value is obtainable by this simple multiple-beam thin-film technique. Good definition has been obtained at × 2000 with collodion films.

There is one further important use of a correctly applied thin-film technique and that is the production of a greatly enhanced interferometric contrast for a general topographical survey. Take for example Plate 128 (× 70). This is a reflection micrograph picture of part of an octahedron face of a diamond. A number of well-delineated trigons appear and in the main open space are faint indications of others. But now compare with this Plate 129 (× 70) for the same region, coated with a very thin balsam film, and viewed by monochromatic light to give two-beam interference. The effect is very striking indeed, and especially in

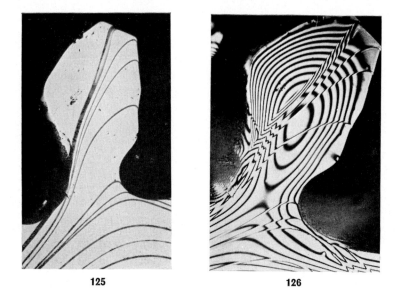

125

126

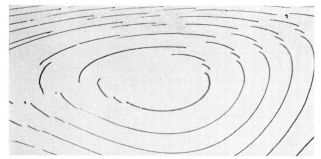

127

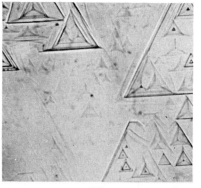

128

129

Plates 125-129

the central region marked new heightened contrasts have been created, showing up a great deal of topographical information.

The thin-film Fizeau fringes suffer from the characteristic defect of all Fizeau fringes when applied to the observation of discontinuities, i.e. direction and order allocation are uncertain. One can use a succession of wavelengths, but the simplest solution is to select one of the steps shown by the Fizeau fringe system and to re-examine it with fringes of equal chromatic order. Even if the film is so thin as to give very high dispersion with white light, this is still adequate for a quick assessment of direction of step and allocation of orders.

To sum up, although the thin-film technique is not of basic importance it is an easy rapid approach for specific problems, especially those in which a region is to be studied not easy of access to an optical flat and of particular use when the detail under study is so small that a very high magnification is needed, with consequent small working distance, and also with consequent necessity of very small interferometric gap. A remarkable example is shown in Plate 359.

The Contouring Efficiency of the Evaporated Silver Film

Basic to the application of multiple-beam interferometry to micro-topography is the implicit acceptance that the thermally evaporated silver film contours the microsurface features with close fidelity, indeed to within virtually molecular dimensions. It was shown in Plates 38–42 that thin silver films have a micro-granular structure which was revealed with the electron microscope, yet as these grains are far below the visual resolution of the optical microscope used for interferometry, to this order of observation the silver film can be treated as continuous. It has been all along assumed in multiple-beam interferometry that the silver film does accurately contour the surface pattern, even down to within a few ångström units although the thicknesses of the silver films used themselves are in the range of from 500 to 1000 ångström units. This assumption as to extreme uniformity of contouring has in the past been strongly justified from several independent lines of evidence. For instance cleavage areas on mica, some square centimetres in extent, were established interferometrically by showing uniform tint areas to be smooth to within the crystal lattice spacing 20 Å. Even a deviation in the silver thickness by a mere $2\frac{1}{2}$ Å would show up as a 10% local change in tint, and this is not observed under ideal conditions. Again, in the early preparation of interference filters (which I developed independently of Geffken in 1942) silver was deposited on to glass, then a layer of cryolite, then silver. If such a filter has good monochromaticity its colour is very uniform and therefore its thickness is closely uniform to within a few ångström units. But the striking fact is that one can make a highly uniform filter with a piece of crude glass, which interferometrically shows numerous hills and dales. This implies a very perfect contouring efficiency, for the first silver layer contours the topography, then the thin cryolite layer contours this to give a layer of uniform thickness, and ultimately the final silver layer again contours the combination accurately. The final filter consists of a thin cryolite film which is far from plane, but its thickness is everywhere highly uniform and so the filter is efficiently everywhere monochromatic.

Then again, step heights both on crystal cleavages and on growth spirals of crystals, have been interferometrically numerically measured which are small integral multiples of the known lattice spacings (often a single lattice). Clearly the silver contouring has not introduced any falsifications and *must be accurate down to within lattice dimensions.* This is a most remarkable feature. This character of accurate local contouring is more important to high magnification microtopography than to the interferometric determination of the thickness of a thin film. In measuring the thickness of a thin film deposited say on glass, the step height is determined by over-depositing on this about 1000 Å of silver, say thickness T. It is then assumed that the original step on the glass due to the film will reappear in the silver film. Now it is reasonable to expect this even if the efficiency of contour is poor at the step edge itself. Measurement for film thickness need not be made near the edge, but away from it and then one can reasonably anticipate that film thickness on the one side will be T and on the other $T + t$ so that the step t reappears. This implies that the silver film does not bed itself within the granularities of the original film and evidence was given formerly that this is so for all but the very thinnest of films. In measuring microtopography the observer can be confronted with sharp edges, which are evidently crystallographically sharp and with regions extending over only 1/100th mm diameter. It becomes necessary to know whether the silver is efficiently contouring such small features also.

Here again there is ample indirect evidence from the numerous and varied interferograms taken which confidently indicate that the contouring is good. Consider for example Plate 130 ($\times$ 180) which illustrates fringes over a spiral on a crystal. The fringes run sharply and crisply up to the spiral boundaries and stop dead. The same has often been seen on mica cleavages. There is neither any suggestion of silver pile-up nor any failure to reach the edge. The contour appears perfect and is in accord with the crystallographic prediction of a crystallographic plane reaching a sharp drop. Even at the edges, the sharp fringe shape justifies a statement that there is certainly accurate contouring here to within less than 0·5 mm on the print, i.e. to within something like at least 1/400th mm on the object. Further, by accurate contouring is meant correct height contouring to better than half a fringe width, i.e. better than 25 Å. One can detect a slight 'pip' at the fringe edge, but this is probably simple optical diffraction. Yet in spite of the confidence given by all these indirect observations it was considered prudent to make some direct measurements of contouring efficiency using the following approach. A small step with very sharp edge is required and on a surface of inherently high reflectivity such that no initial overcoating with silver is needed. Then a layer of silver of known thickness is deposited on this and the step remeasured. Increasing layers of silver are deposited and the step remeasured each time. If contouring is adequate the step should remain the same for thicker and thicker over-layers. It should also be the same close to the step edge, and away from the edge.

It may be objected that there is a defect here in that the thickness of the silver over-layer is to be determined by the very method under examination, but this is of no consequence at all. For indeed if the contouring is imperfect, all this means is that our assessments of the particular overlayer thicknesses need correction and this is a secondary consideration. Again, if it turns out that the contouring is perfect, even this minor correction will not arise. Quite independently of qualitative measurement the experiment will give a definite quantitative answer as to whether contouring is adequate or not. In fact, as will now be shown, the contouring by evaporated silver is astonishingly precise.

Experimental Study of Contouring. The problem before us is to find a perfectly sharp step on a perfectly smooth flat face. Clearly the production of such a step edge by any mechanical or artificial means introduces formidable difficulties. The step must be very robust, since it can be anticipated that the frequent removal and deposition of silver on the surface will be required. Nature fortunately has presented us with the ideal solution to the problem in the growth spirals on silicon carbide. Here we have a material which exhibits perfect steps, between molecularly smooth surfaces, on an adequate scale, a material of great strength and hardness and with a natural high specular reflectivity. It fulfils all requirements.

The spiral selected for this study is shown in Plate 131 (× 60). It was chosen because of : (*a*) the very wide spacing between the loops (about 0·4 mm between inner loops) ; (*b*) the surface was found to be of

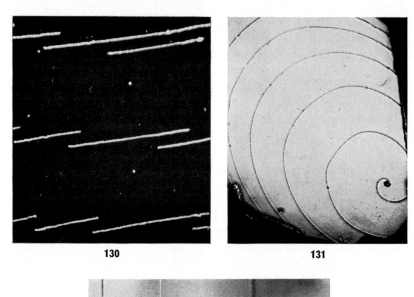

130

131

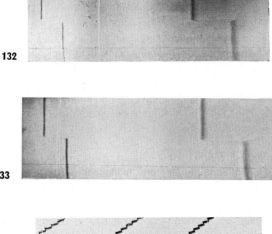

132

133

134

Plates 130-134

perfect quality between the loops ; and (c) the step height was ideal for exact measurement. The second loop was selected and the step height found to be 480 Å, with an error certainly no more than $\pm$ 3 Å, if that.

A layer of silver was deposited on the crystal and its thickness measured by having alongside a piece of glass which received a film of the same thickness over half its area. The thickness was measured interferometrically. Any contouring defect will only have the second-order effect of giving a wrong thickness value but this will not influence the real test, which is the repeated re-evaluation of the crystal step thickness when coated with different thicknesses of silver. The crystal step was measured at two different points, one as near the edge as possible, the other nearly a tenth of a millimetre from the edge.

In making a precision determination of step height the fringes of equal chromatic order are advantages since they give the step locally and, furthermore, any variation in dispersion due to the spiral pattern does not introduce complications or errors.

The silver was deposited in a vacuum approaching 10^{-6} mmHg, the distance between the hot source of silver and the receiving surface being 35 cm. Typical fringes of equal chromatic order using very high dispersion are shown in Plate 132 ($\times$ 75) for the step edge when the measured overlayer film thickness is 845 Å, and in Plate 133 ($\times$ 75) for an overlayer of 2800 Å thick. Fringes at the red (left) end are very sharp and the step height can be measured with considerable confidence. Measured step heights for a series of film thicknesses are shown as follows, measured for a point 0·06 mm from the step edge.

Ag film thickness, Å	255	520	1205	2800	5800	7000	10,000	13,500	26,700
Measured step, Å	479	482	477	479	482	484	478	483	477
Difference from 480 Å	-1	$+2$	-3	-1	$+2$	$+4$	-2	$+3$	-3

These are remarkable results, for it is seen that the step is constantly 480 Å to within the estimated experimental error of $\pm$ 3 Å. This is true, even for a silver layer thickness of as much as 26,700 Å which is actually *56 times as thick* as the step height itself.

For measurements made as near as possible to the edge itself a difference begins to appear in accordance with the following :

Ag film thickness, Å	255	520	1205	2800	5800	7000	10,000	13,500	26,700
Measured step, Å	479	482	475	478	483	475	467	438	383
Difference from 480 Å	− 1	+ 2	− 5	− 2	+ 3	− 5	− 13	− 42	− 97

Up to a silver film thickness of some 6000 Å the contour is still exact, i.e. the step is still effectively 480 Å. But after this the step steadily falls and is almost 100 Å too small by the time the silver film thickness has reached 26,700 Å.

The failure in step-value depends upon the distance from the edge. For the 26,700 Å film, deviation is 97 Å at the edge. Fig. 31 shows how

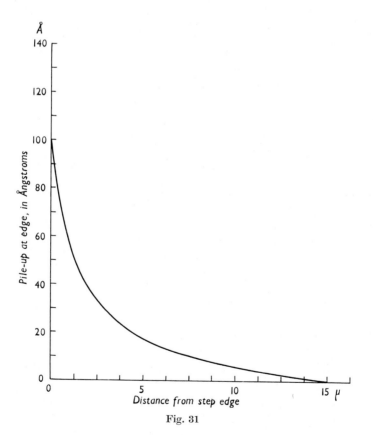

Fig. 31

the departure diminishes on moving away from the edge. At 15μ from the edge there is no deviation, but the deviation progressively increases, as the edge is approached, until very close to the edge the error is about 100 Å. It is evident that with the very thick deposit a preferential pile-up is taking place on the lower tread of the step. These two sets of data permit the following conclusions to be drawn. *Up to a deposited over-layer thickness of 6000 A the contour is effectively perfect even very close to the step edge.* It is still effectively perfect (to within the 3 Å error) at a thickness up to 26,700 Å for all distances beyond 0·015 mm from the edge. Now the importance of these findings lies in the fact that good interferometric silvering always lies in the range 500 to 1000 Å. The lower figure gives an excellent reflectivity for much work and the upper figure is an effectively opaque film suitable for maximum reflectivity for the rear face in reflection interferometry. Clearly the measurement proves that for such film thickness the contouring is perfect. These precise direct numerical data confirm what had been indirectly inferred earlier.

Multilayer Dielectric Films

It has already been pointed out that there are distinct advantages in reflection interferometry secured by the use of a multilayer dielectric reflector on the top surface, i.e. that nearest the microscope objective. The extremely low absorption, coupled to the very high reflectivity (97%) gives fringes of extreme narrowness and of very high contrast. Many of the high-quality fringe patterns illustrated in this work were obtained with such multilayers. The best attainable fringe definition is secured when the reflectivity on *both* surfaces is at its highest, ideally then both faces should be covered with multilayer. But this at once raises the question of the contouring efficiency of a multilayer. A multilayer may often consist of nine layers, of alternate quarter-wave thickness (optically) of zinc sulphide and cryolite. Taking the refractive indices into consideration this gives, for λ 5461, a thickness of 570 Å for each of five zinc sulphide layers and an additional four layers of cryolite each of 1000 Å thick. The total metrical thickness of such a multilayer adds up to the relatively considerable amount of almost 7000 Å. This quantity exceeds the 6000 Å limit imposed on silver, and in any case *a priori* one might anticipate that a multiple deposited complex layer would assuredly not contour as well as a single layer, even of the same thickness as the complex.

To examine the properties of the multilayer we have determined separately the contouring characteristics of both zinc sulphide and cryolite independently, using the same 480 Å step spiral on silicon carbide. The experiments were more elaborate since after deposit of the film of cryolite or zinc sulphide it was then necessary to deposit a 700 Å coating of silver on the cryolite or zinc sulphide in order to have the necessary high reflectivity for sharp multiple-beam fringes.

As before, repeated measurements with increasing film thickness were made, but it soon became evident that it was not necessary to go to such high value of film thickness. Again as before two sets of step values were assessed, one set 0·06 mm from the edge, the other set very close to the edge. At the 0·06-mm point the step heights found for the known 480 Å step are as follows for zinc sulphide :

Zinc sulphide thickness, Å	304	730	1400	2700	3600	7220	12,750	16,400
Step height measured, Å	478	481	483	479	477	484	474	476
Deviation from 480 Å	− 2	+ 1	+ 3	− 1	− 3	+ 4	− 6	− 4

Contouring is adequate, certainly up to 7000 Å and not seriously in error by 16,000 Å. Near the edge itself there is, as expected, a discrepancy as shown by the following table :

Zinc sulphide thickness, Å	304	730	1400	2700	3600	7220	12,750	16,400
Step height measured, Å	478	479	480	479	468	452	418	408
Deviation from 480 Å	− 2	− 1	0	− 1	− 12	− 38	− 62	− 72

An error establishes itself at about 3000 Å thickness of zinc-sulphide film and increases steadily beyond that point.

The deviations found for cryolite films are even more marked. Measurements at 0·06 mm from the edge give the following :

Cryolite film thickness, Å	265	980	1540	1750	2950	5200	9300	10,170
Step height measured, Å	480	483	485	487	485	478	477	483
Deviation from 480 Å	0	+ 3	+ 5	+ 7	+ 5	− 2	− 3	+ 3

The scatter is larger than in the other data, yet the contour appears adequate up to a cryolite thickness of 10,000 Å.

The deviations near to the edge are shown by the following table :

Cryolite film thickness, Å	265	980	1540	1750	2950	5200	9300	10,170
Step height measured, Å	480	482	482	476	458	428	426	420
Deviation from 480 Å	0	+ 2	+ 2	− 4	− 22	− 52	− 54	− 60

It is clear that failure now sets in at about 2000 Å and by 10,000 Å it is some five times as great as with the corresponding thickness in silver films.

It is true that four separate 1000 Å layers of cryolite may differ from a single 4000 Å layer, but the conclusion seems to be forced on us that there are inherent contouring dangers in the use of a multilayer on a surface whose topography is under study. Fortunately the absorption coefficient only plays its vital role on the *first surface*, i.e. on the matching flat. Hence the best possible arrangement is to coat the optical flat with a multilayer and to coat the surface under study with silver. This arrangement secures the best of both types of coating, the low absorption and high reflectivity on the flat and the excellent contouring property and high reflectivity on the object under study from the silver.

Test shows that multilayers lead to slight blurring on step edges. Plate 134 (× 70) shows the pattern given by part of a stepped spiral of height 168 Å, which has been coated with a nine-multilayer film. Contrast is extremely good, but on the original negative a smear blurr effect is clearly noticeable at each step edge. Compare for instance the crisp edge in Plate 130 despite the fact that Plate 130 is at magnification × 150 compared with Plate 134 at × 70.

In reviewing these experiments on the contouring efficiency of silver and the multilayer complexes, the following comments may be appropriate. It is known that silver when it first strikes a surface exhibits lateral mobility. No doubt this two-dimensional mobility leads to a most efficient contouring by the very early layers and then the succeeding contour builds up faithfully. The pile-up, which we observe at very high thickness of overlay of silver, may be attributable to a surface mobility effect. There is just another slight possibility which should be perhaps taken into consideration. We have here a case of atoms impinging on to a perfect crystal surface and there may be some slight true atomic-wave diffraction. This could possibly lead to slight deflection and a pile-up of the kind observed. If this is a contributory factor then the pile-up would not appear on non-crystalline material, such as glasses, plastics, etc. This is, however, merely a tentative conjecture with little to support it.

REFERENCES

Nos. 37, 38, K, 50, T.

PART FOUR

CRYSTAL CLEAVAGES
ETCHING OF CRYSTALS
MODULATED INTERFERENCE FRINGES

11. STUDIES ON CRYSTAL CLEAVAGES

*Diamond — Crystallographic traces — Selenite — Galena — Mica —
Bismuth — References.*

Cleavage of Diamond

THE cleavage of diamond is a subject which has stimulated a formidable amount of research. Here only some of the findings secured by interferometry will be briefly surveyed.

It has been known for many centuries that diamond cleaves easily parallel to the (111) plane and it has been variously claimed that it has secondary cleavages parallel to cubic and rhombic dodecahedron planes. These latter we have substantiated by our studies on the induction of percussion marks which will be described later. The professional diamond cleaver hesitates to attempt cleavage in any direction other than (111). This easy (111) cleavage was first attributed by Ewald in 1914 to the two possible spacings in the octahedron plane, one layer being spaced such as to have only a third of the valence bonds per atom compared with the other.

Some hundreds of diamond cleavage faces have been studied by us interferometrically, and from this some general conclusions have emerged. First we have found a marked distinction in cleavage between the diamonds usually classed as Type I and Type II.

It has been known since 1934 that diamonds can be divided into two broad groups (these groups can be further subdivided) which show differences in their infra-red and ultra-violet transmission and absorption characteristics. That called Type I cuts off the ultra-violet spectrum at about λ 3000 Å, but Type II transmits down to as far as λ 2250 Å.

The Type I cleavage, when examined by interferometry, turns out to be very rough indeed, and often hardly repays study interferometrically. Typical are the transmission fringes for a whole cleavage face shown in Plate 135 ($\times$ 25). The cleavage is almost conchoidal in character, very rough compared with a good cleavage. Little can be inferred, other than the fact that some regions are less rough than others. A selected region on one cleavage, shown in Plate 136 ($\times$ 25), shows an irregular criss-cross of cleavage steps in what was an exceptionally good region of an otherwise very rough surface.

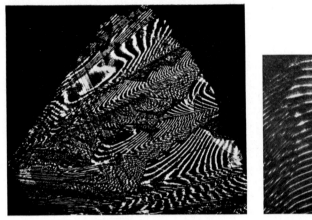

135

136

137

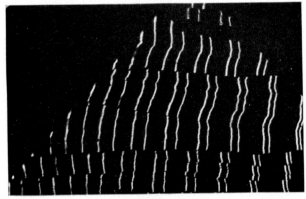

138

Plates 135-138

Now in comparison Type II crystals can, and at times do, show an entirely different kind of cleavage. Plate 137 ($\times$ 80) shows a corner of a Type II crystal and the interference pattern (in transmission) for this region is shown in Plate 138 ($\times$ 100). This photograph has been taken in transmission with the two yellow mercury lines, and the fringes appear in pairs, permitting allocation of orders for the steps. The smooth character of this type of cleavage is entirely different in nature from that shown by the quite typical Type I crystal on Plate 135. Step heights observed on Plate 138 vary from 100 to 2000 Å. In contradistinction to what is found in mica, step height varies *along* a cleavage line and in one instance, for example, within a range of half a millimetre on the surface, the step changed from 990 Å to 770 Å. Thus the regions on either side of a step are not parallel planes but slightly inclined, by amounts easily computed from the interferograms.

A high magnification picture of fringes of equal chromatic order across part of that crystal surface shown in Plate 137 is reproduced in Plate 139 ($\times$ 500) and this region is undoubtedly superior in uniformity to the Type I cleavage surfaces.

Crystallographic Traces. One striking feature regularly observed by us when examining cleaved diamonds is the appearance on the cleavage face of strictly oriented but quite faint *traces*, usually in (111) directions. These undoubtedly represent traces of original growth sheets which have been cut through by the cleavage. It is always found that an interferogram shows a marked kink effect at such a trace. Plate 140 ($\times$ 70) shows part of a cleavage of a Type II diamond. A well-marked trace runs horizontally across the middle of the picture and there are many others parallel to this one. Plate 141 ($\times$ 70), the interferogram for this region, reveals numerous features of interest, namely : (*a*) in accordance with our usual observations for Type II, the areas between the cleavage lines are of good smooth quality ; (*b*) the ' river '-like formations are shown by the fringes to be regular sequences of steps ; and (*c*) where the fringes pass over the central linear trace there is a curvature with a kinked ridge.

This region is *concavely* curved and this is shown to advantage by Plate 142 ($\times$ 80) in which are illustrated fringes of equal chromatic order taken over part of the kinked region. These show up well the shape of the kink, which occurs along the crystallographic trace. There is probably a definite discontinuity here as well, as will be established later, in the discussion of etching experiments, but for the sake of comparison at this point Plate 143 ($\times$ 70) is shown. This will readily be recognized as the right-hand side of the same surface as that on Plate 140.

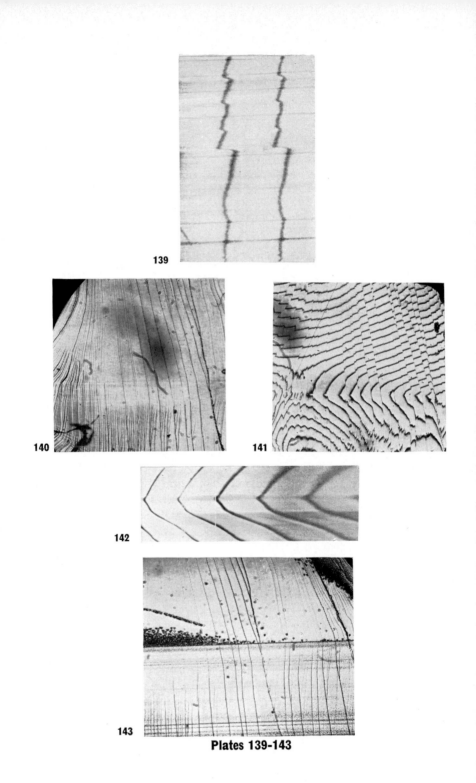

139

140

141

142

143

Plates 139-143

It has been etched, as already described. It is seen that all the traces have been strongly developed up. Etching has acted preferentially on the trace regions, which are linear boundaries. The etching shows up differentially on either side of the linear trace and it must be concluded from this that the concentration of dislocations or impurities changes abruptly at the trace boundary.

Cleavage of Selenite

The cleavage of selenite bears a superficial resemblance to that of mica, but interferometry reveals a very clear difference. Plates 144 (× 60) and 145 (× 60) are characteristic interferograms for selenite cleavages. As in mica there are hills and dales and well-marked cleavage lines. Indeed the patterns have a reasonably close resemblance to those of poor-quality micas, but a closer inspection reveals a very real difference in secondary microstructure. A particularly striking characteristic of mica is the remarkable smoothness of the fringes. The surfaces may well be wrinkled but the fringe smoothness is almost invariably remarkably true.

On the contrary the fringes of selenite exhibit a very broken structure. Compare for instance the two patterns Plate 146 (× 60) and Plate 147 (× 60) shown alongside. Plate 146 refers to mica and Plate 147 to selenite. The selenite fringes are broken and ragged. This effect is shown up even more so by the fringes of equal chromatic order, Plate 148 (× 90), on a typical relatively *good* area on selenite. The whole surface shows a mass of secondary cleavage elements, which vary in step from 300 Å down to less than 20 Å.

Cleavage of Galena

The cleavage of galena is typically deceptive (just as is that of Type I diamond). Galena cleaves so easily that one might have anticipated the cleavage surfaces to be of good quality. A few good examples of a Wisconsin galena which were under examination for semi-conducting properties were cleaved and examined by interferometry. This crystal had 6×10^{16} p-type centres per cm^3. Interferometrically the cleavage was most disappointing. Plate 149 (× 100) shows the region near an edge of a crystal block, cleaved out. A block pattern is apparent. The blocks are neither flat, nor are their surfaces parallel. This is a fairly characteristic picture and many like it have been obtained from different samples.

One unusually bright face, when examined, gave a much superior interferogram as shown in Plate 150 (× 100). On this are both primary

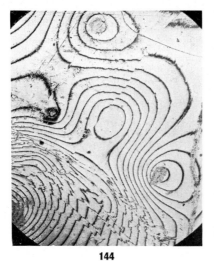

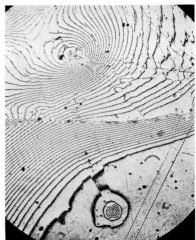

144   145

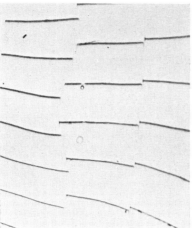

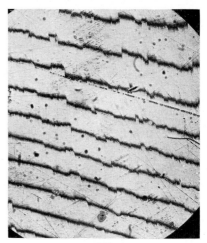

146   147

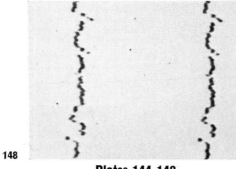

148

Plates 144-148

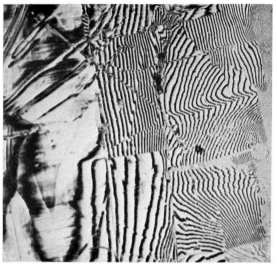

149

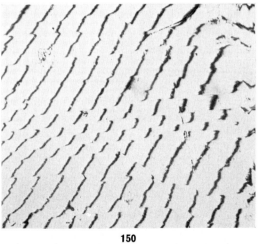

150

Plates 149, 150

cleavage strips and within these a secondary fine structure. Cleavage lines are not always parallel nor at right angles, as might at first have been expected from the way the crystal cleaves into parallelopipeds. Nor are the faces of the strips parallel, but at times inclined, dipping down or rising up. Clearly the crystal is relatively very imperfect and one can conclude that the interferograms are revealing a lineage block pattern or a large-scale mosaic complex.

Cleavage of Mica

The cleavage of mica has already been discussed in various chapters. Here brief comment is made on matching only. Measurement shows close agreement (to within 4 Å) for the steps on the two matched faces of mica cleavages and it is readily established that there is exact keying in of the two surfaces.

A rare example of a cleavage through a small crystal inclusion is shown in Plate 151 (× 50) where the fringes run up to and reveal a small parallelopiped inclusion.

Matched mica cleavages have also been studied by an etching method which turns out to be an immensely powerful technique supplementing the findings of interferometry. This method of etch has also been applied to the study of matched cleavages in diamond and this approach is of sufficient interest to justify a later section on its own.

The Cleavage on a Bismuth Crystal

Single crystals of bismuth can be cleaved fairly easily and the cleavage surfaces which have good reflectivity repay interferometric study. Interferograms on cleavage regions on single crystals of bismuth are shown in Plate 152 (× 70) and Plate 153 (× 70). These have been arranged with different dispersions since the surface shows two quite distinctive features. By comparing the two dispersions it is seen that the surface has a saw-tooth pattern. Alternate regions are parallel to each other. In Plate 152 the matching flat is placed nearly parallel to one of these alternate sets of surfaces so that dispersion is high in these. The second set are also parallel to each other, but all are inclined to the other faces at a small angle of about $1\frac{1}{4}°$. These regions are definitely not cleavage step discontinuities of the kind normally seen on non-metal crystals. They form essentially a saw-tooth ridge, as seen perhaps better on Plate 153.

The normal type of cleavage discontinuity does exist, but the cleavage lines are those which run more or less at right angles to the ridge pattern.

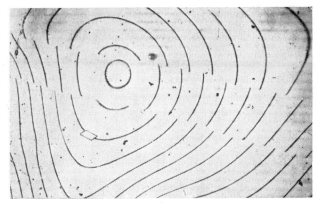

151

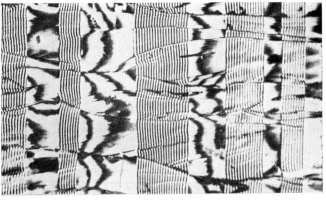

152

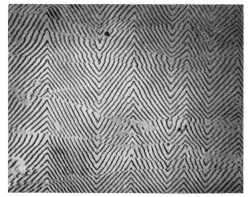

153

Plates 151-153

The discontinuities can be seen to advantage on Plate 153 in which the steps are seen to be of the familiar type.

Noteworthy is the quality of the surface between cleavage steps. Although relatively smooth, it can be seen from Plate 152 that the areas between the cleavage lines are slightly convex. Some of the heights of the cleavage steps are of the order of a fringe width, in this case say 100 Å.

References

Nos. G, 54, Z.

12. MATCHED CLEAVAGES

The study of matched cleavages—Topaz—Matched cleavage faces—Calcite—Reference.

The Study of Matched Cleavages

A VARIETY of theories have been proposed to explain crystal cleavage. Cleavage varies from crystal to crystal and ranges from what is described as the perfect to the difficult. Various cleavage rules have been proposed. It seems that cleavage planes are always planes of high density of atomic packing, in which molecular or atomic cohesion is strong, but is weak at right angles to this plane. As a rule cleavage planes contain whole molecules and, in cleavage, radicals generally remain intact. Many cleavages traditionally described in the texts as perfect have been found by us using interferometry to be very imperfect on an interferometric scale, but some of the cleavages studied, notably those of mica, topaz and calcite, can cleave very perfectly indeed.

No one has apparently questioned whether there is any difference between the two oppositely matched faces separated by cleavage. It has apparently been taken for granted that the two faces key together exactly. This is but one of the aspects of cleavage we have studied with interferometry. Again, ordinary simple cleavage studies have neglected what might be called the fine-structure microtopography of cleavage. For instance, historically, selenite and mica were at an early date confused because they both cleave in similar thin flakes which superficially resemble each other. Yet the typical interferometric comparison of mica and selenite cleavages as shown in Plate 146 and Plate 147 reveal strongly marked differences, such that they could never be confused with one another.

One of the most reputedly perfect of all cleavages is that of topaz, and some examples of this will now be considered.

Topaz

Topaz is a very hard crystal and cleaves on the basal (001) plane. Its hardness, Mohs number 8, is advantageous from the viewpoint of interferometry. Topaz crystals were cleaved and the freshly exposed surfaces silvered to permit of interferograms being taken. A basic

147

object of this investigation was to compare the two opposite matched faces produced by the cleavage. Despite the long-recognized perfect cleavage of topaz, the first crystal examined had on the cleavage faces several high projections, i.e. they were very far from plane, so much so that it was necessary to use the micro-flat technique in order to secure close enough approach for high definition.

The topaz cleavage faces showed several distinctive characteristics. Consider Plate 154 (× 90). This shows a number of remarkably plane regions separated by curved cleavage lines. The plane areas are of striking perfection and one extended over no less than 9 sq mm. In these regions, which tend to be long narrow strips, the cleaved surface appears to be a close approximation to a true plane and it can safely be argued that cleavage is true to within a single lattice spacing. Any observed deviations are undoubtedly due to the matching surface.

A second feature is the occasional appearance of regular descending (or ascending) steps, an example of which is shown in Plate 155 (× 90). Yet in general step heights differ in an arbitrary fashion both up and down. They vary in value from less than 50 Å to at least 1200 Å. The X-ray lattice separation for cleavage planes is 8·8 Å and we have some (uncertain) evidence that the observed steps are possibly integral multiples of this, but our accuracy is not really sufficient to be categorical.

In the majority of cases the step height remains quite constant along the length of a cleavage line, but there are occasional striking departures, in which a cleavage line (or line pairs) terminates in the surface. These will be discussed in what follows on the consideration of oppositely matched faces.

Matched Cleavage Faces

When two oppositely cleaved faces are matched we find that they key perfectly. Thus Plate 156 (× 50) and Plate 157 (× 50) show two matched regions from opposing faces. They are exact mirror images. Below each, in Plate 158 (× 50) and Plate 159 (× 50), are shown the corresponding interferograms. Now it will be remembered that the pattern seen on an interferogram depends entirely on the relative setting between the crystal and the optical flat. Thus in general the two interferograms *appear* to be different. What does matter is not the particular pattern, but the numerical values of the steps obtained from each interferogram and the general dispersion pattern. When this is taken into account the interferometric patterns are seen to key exactly

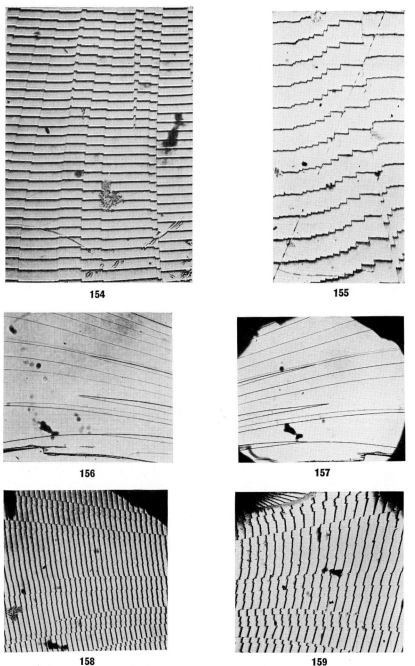

154

155

156

157

158

159

Plates 154-159

into each other, an up-step on the one side being matched by an exactly equal and opposite down-step on the other. An incidental conclusion is that during the cleavage no material has been flaked off in micro-fashion and lost. Such a flaking mechanism has sometimes been found by us on cleavages of other crystals, a piece being clearly missing from one matched cleavage face.

Of particular interest is the appearance in both Plate 156 and Plate 157 of two well-marked V surface terminating patterns. On the one face the V-shape is a depression and on the other an elevation. It is impor-tant to note that the step height does *not* run down to zero at the terminating V tip. On the contrary, in one particular instance, where the step is some 900 Å the step value maintains itself reasonably well over a whole length of 0·33 mm from the V tip outwards. Clearly this is not a case of spiral or screwing dislocation step sloping up from below and terminating in the surface. It is a case of a V-shaped block torn out, with the V base still in the normal crystallographic cleavage plane.

That in general the matching of the steps at corresponding points is good is shown by direct measurement. Taking three steps at random the oppositely paired values found are (1) 532 Å, 541 Å (2) 892 Å, 898 Å (3) 303 Å, 308 Å. The differences, 9, 6, and 5 Å are not significant in interferograms with this particular dispersion and the steps can therefore be considered as identical.

The tearing out of quite narrow V pieces is common and care must be taken in identifying such, otherwise an apparent mismatch between steps on opposite faces can be assessed. As regards interpretation, it is possible that there is a terminating dislocation at the tip of the V, or alternatively the V is evidence of a mosaic block structure.

Calcite

Calcite is always described in texts as having a perfect rhombohedral cleavage in (1011) and this material offers another opportunity for comparing matched cleavages. The softness of the material imposes careful limitations and once silvered, a calcite surface cannot be re-cleaned for a second examination. The unit lattice cell, 6 Å, is too small for direct identification by interferometry.

The cleavage, without interferometry, somewhat resembles topaz, but interferograms reveal a considerable difference. Calcite shows a complex microstructure with complex terminations of cleavage lines in the surface. Plate 160 (× 60) and Plate 161 (× 60) are characteristic examples, from different crystals. Plate 160 shows a regular step formation, yet there are frequent complex V patterns. Plate 161

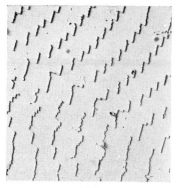

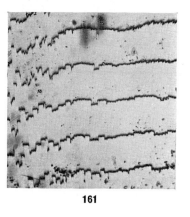

160

161

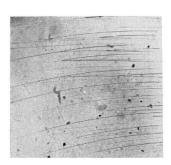

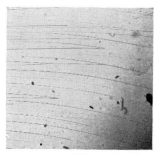

162

163

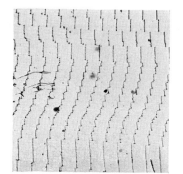

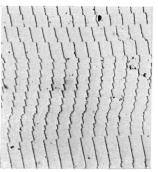

164

165

166

Plates 160-166

shows the micro-structure on the crystal. The whole surface is a broken set of fine cleavage steps, many in V pattern.

With regard to matching, there is usually very close correlation as shown by the two matched micrographs in Plate 162 (× 25) and Plate 163 (× 25) which reveal a full distribution of V patterns. Interferograms for a less complex region with matched cleavages, are shown in Plate 164 (× 35) and Plate 165 (× 35). The various steps on the matched patterns are identical within the 10 Å limit of measurement, but in one case, at top right in Plate 165, where a small black patch indicates an inclusion, the fringe on the Plate 164 is straight and on Plate 165 curved as if a small piece were missing. The secondary structure is not as noticeable as in Plate 160, in which both lateral magnification and interferometric dispersion are higher.

Although a single lattice step is not measurable, the steps shown in Plate 166 (× 70) are of much interest. Fringes of equal chromatic order in transmission are shown taken over a small strip on calcite. The upper step between the upper region and the central short narrow strip is 72 Å. That between the lower region and the central strip is 60 Å. Thus the main lower and upper strips are displaced exactly 12 Å. It will be seen that these steps are just 12, 10 and 2 lattice spacings. This establishes that the steps are small integral values of the lattice, even although this is only a mere 6 Å.

REFERENCE

Letter O.

13. ETCHING OF CLEAVAGES

Mica—Diamond—Crystallographic traces—References.

The Etching of Matched Mica Cleavages

It has already been established that a good muscovite mica can cleave true to a single lattice over some square centimetres. It can be conjectured that such a surface might well be relatively free from dislocations. There are reasons for believing that a delicate light etch can preferentially attack dislocations, faults or raised ledges, thus a selected mica appeared a suitable material for etch studies. In all our experiments etching was controlled to be very slow. The mica was exposed to the vapour from a solution of hydrofluoric acid and even the largest etch pits formed, which, where only 1/20th mm in length, took some 48 hours to develop. The slow controlled etch is essential, for if the etch develops too rapidly it (*a*) does not distinguish between large and small steps, and (*b*) soon destroys the whole surface and thus erodes the very details sought for.

A highly perfect quality of Australian Rex Mine muscovite mica was selected ; a typical interferogram, Plate 167 (× 60) shows how very smooth and perfect is the initial surface quality. When such a sample is etched, two clearly differentiated types of etch effect occur (there is a third less obvious effect, as will be shown later). Plate 168 (× 120) is typical. It shows a group of cleavage lines, which are quite strongly delineated (see later). Two distinct kinds of etch pit are present. There are three isolated oriented rhomb-shaped pits, more or less of the same size, but in addition the whole background is covered with a multitude of smaller rhomb-shaped very shallow pits, all oriented the same way but all running into each other. These produce a great surface roughening which is shown by the interference pattern in Plate 169 (× 35) over what had been an area as perfect as that on Plate 167 regarding surface quality, and only had one single cleavage step on it near the top right corner. Pits can be seen and depths are obtainable from the fringes. The general enormous fringe broadening should be compared with that of Plate 167. The fringe width is nearly a third of a whole order in some parts which means that the surface roughness extends over some 900 Å in depth. For it will be recognized that just as the fringe character on Plate 53 gave a measure of the depths of trigons, so the roughened surface here also leads to a fringe broadening which is a measure of the depth of the roughness. If we imagine a corrugated surface, then for a given order of interference, the same optical path between matching flat and surface is formed on regions adjacent to the position where the sharp fringe would normally appear between smooth surfaces. So fringe broadening becomes a direct measure of the height of the surface irregularities.

When matched cleavages of mica are etched remarkable results are obtained when the isolated pits are compared on the opposite faces. Plate 170 ($\times$ 50) and Plate 171 ($\times$ 50) illustrate two exactly matched areas. *There is one-to-one correspondence between the position and size of the pits.* The sizes may differ slightly, but their centres are in exact correspondence. *The two patterns are mirror images.* An occasional ' rogue ' can appear on one side and not on the other, but such is a rarity.

Clearly the cleavage has broken through impurity or dislocation centres which are common to both sides and the pits have nucleated at these common centres. There is one other feature of considerable interest and that concerns the long dark cleavage line. For it is seen, first that the line is of different thickness on the two pictures, but much more significant, the lines and etch pit pattern relatively are displaced. Thus in Plate 171 the line cuts a pit, at the top, but in Plate 170 the displacement is clearly evident for the line is now to the left of the pit.

By reference to marks on the *back* of the mica it is readily established that it is the dark cleavage line and not the etch pit pattern which has displaced. By superposing (in reverse) the two negatives of Plates 170 and 171 and printing through the combination, the print obtained is that shown in Plate 172 ($\times$ 50). Here the pits are superposed and it is at once apparent that the two cleavage lines have separated. The mechanism is in fact self-evident as etching attacks the raised ledge. It attacks it at the same rate as it attacks the ledge which represents the sides of a pit. A step-up on the one face is a step-down on the other. Etch attacks the upper edges on each. One edge must move to the right, relative to the pits, the other to the left. The separation between the lines will be about the same as the separation of the sides of the pits. Thus it is established that there are three etching mechanisms : (*a*) general micro-surface solution by micro pits ; (*b*) eating away of raised ledges ; and (*c*) development of isolated pits originating at common nucleation centres. These grow essentially by lateral dissolu-

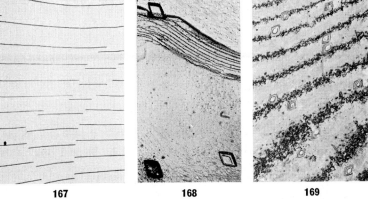

167 **168** **169**

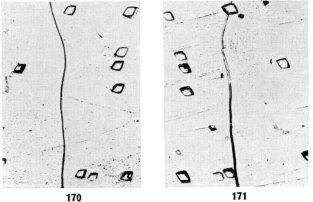

170 **171**

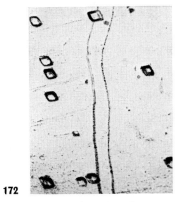

172

Plates 167-172

tion of the edges, at a rate similar to the dissolution of the ledges in method (*b*).

These findings on mica cleavages gave a clue to the explanation of the complex etching patterns found on the diamond cleavages to be discussed in the following section.

Diamond Cleavages

The interferometric and etch study of matched cleavages of diamond has revealed much of considerable interest. The Type I diamonds are so rough that investigation of their cleavages is not very profitable. It has also been found that small pieces are occasionally missing from one face or another after the cleavage blow has taken place. These are often small equilateral triangular platelets which have been forced out and lost. The Type II crystals on the other hand usually give sufficiently good cleavages to enable matching studies to be made.

Plate 173 ($\times$ 25) and Plate 174 ($\times$ 25) show two oppositely matched diamond cleavages and in Plate 175 ($\times$ 37) and Plate 176 ($\times$ 37) are the corresponding interferograms. In general there is fairly close correlation between the matched cleavages, yet there are often notable discrepancies. From the same crystal are shown two matched regions in Plate 177 ($\times$ 37) and Plate 178 ($\times$ 37). These have been very carefully matched, yet there are numerous differences. Thus in one region where fringes are almost smooth, the corresponding region on the opposite side is quite hackled. A major difference is seen towards the lower middle left of Plate 178. There is a very jagged area extending over about half an order but there is no corresponding area in Plate 177. Careful examination reveals numerous minor discrepancies. In this respect diamond is different to most other cleavages so far studied. Even Type II diamonds are poor cleavers compared with topaz or mica.

Crystallographic Traces. Attention has already been drawn in Plates 140 to 143 to the curious crystallographic traces seen often on diamond cleavages. It was pointed out then that these linear oriented traces are best studied by etching. Here we establish first that the traces are accurately matched on opposite faces. They are quite distinct from cleavage lines. Plate 179 ($\times$ 70) and Plate 180 ($\times$ 70) are matched diamond cleavages. The pictures were taken with a sensitive phase contrast microscope and the crystallographic traces, usually hard to see, are very clearly defined.

To examine their character interferograms were taken. Plate 181 ($\times$ 40) shows a Fizeau fringe picture over the traces of Plate 179. The interpretation is confused by the fact that the surface is convex but

173

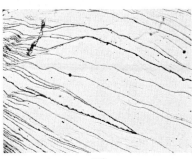

174

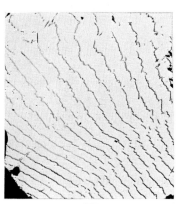

175

176

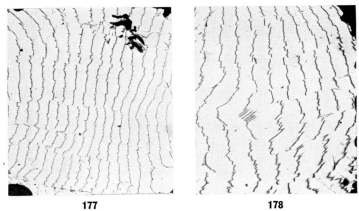

177

178

Plates 173-178

179

180

182

181

183

184

Plates 179-184

what is clearly revealed is that the major traces leave very sharp kinks in the surface which are ridges perhaps half a light wave in height. It is equally clear that the height of the ridge and the ' roof top ' angle vary regularly along a trace. These data are better secured with fringes of equal chromatic order and Plate 182 (× 80) shows high dispersion fringes taken at one region on a trace. These fringes show up a fine structure which is on a very small scale indeed for there exist secondary steps with small dimensions. The roof top angle along one of the major traces varies regularly from 4′ to 10′ of arc.

An astonishing effect is produced by the etching of these matched faces and the etch patterns for Plate 179 and Plate 180 are shown in Plate 183 (× 40) and Plate 184 (× 40). Here it is seen that there are vast numbers of etch pits, but *preferential attack has taken place at the traces*. Whilst the fringe pattern of Plate 181 only really shows up the major traces, the etch reveals a complex fine structure, much more complex than that shown by even very delicate phase-contrast microscopy or by sensitive interferometry. The sensitivity of the etch to picking out and developing subtle surface features is truly remarkable.

These traces are undoubtedly the ' ghosts ' of original growth sheets. so once again the etch reveals the stratigraphy of the original growth. The etch patterns, just as on the cubic faces formerly discussed, appear in three distinct forms : (*a*) close packed regions ; (*b*) linear arrays ; and (*c*) isolated pits (larger than the others) and always situated in resistant areas which are relatively free from etch attack. The one-to-one correspondence between the patterns shown by matched cleavages is astonishing in its perfection.

The remarkable general correspondence of etched patterns on matched cleavages is shown by Plate 185 (× 170) and Plate 186 (× 270). The complex patterns are exact mirror images of each other. The same one-to-one correspondence applies to the isolated pits. Plate 187 (× 1000) and Plate 188 (× 1000) show two matched regions under high magnification. The higher power reveals many properties. In these two matched cleavages the first point to notice is that each isolated pit has its counterpart. They are of course oppositely oriented since the two matched cleavages are opposite (111) faces.

A notable feature is that the cleavage lines are displaced, exactly as was the case with mica. Thus the isolated etch pit at the top of Plate 187 intersects a cleavage line, but this same cleavage line on Plate 188 is displaced *below* the pit. Thus solution has taken place at the cleavage edges exactly as was the case with mica. Another point of interest concerns the departure from symmetry of the etch pits on the vertical

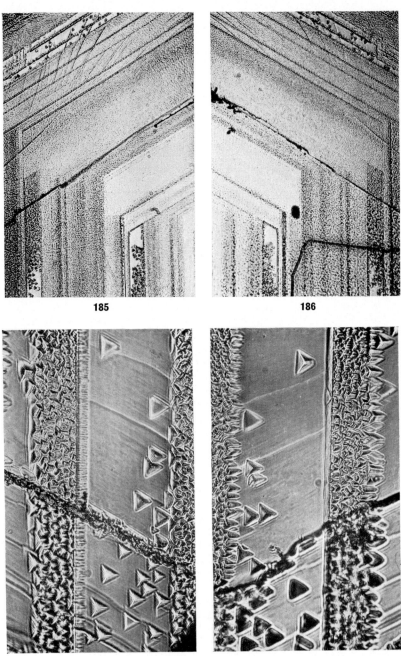

185

186

187

188

Plates 185-188

boundary lines of the pattern. The pits alternately elongate and compress as one moves horizontally across the picture from one vertical boundary line to the next. This is because the boundary is a stepped region and the pit shape differs according to whether it is a rising or falling tread. Thus it is that the asymmetries on the matched patterns are in opposition for clearly a rising tread on the one face is a falling tread on the other.

It may be mentioned here that by cleaving out a small block and etching this, it has been proved that this type of stratigraphy can go right *through* the crystal. The stratigraphy is a record of the history of the growth of diamond, and as such offers valuable information about the interior.

REFERENCES

Nos. 53, 54, Z.

14. MODULATED MULTIPLE-BEAM FRINGES

In some preliminary experiments aimed at the examination of thin biological specimens by multiple-beam methods, some thin transparent cellular biological material was placed between silvered optical flats and localized multiple-beam monochromatic Fizeau fringes were formed. The pattern obtained was puzzling and anomalously complex. A more detailed study was thereupon delegated to A. M. Glauert whose experiments threw light on a complex situation which in fact arises through a modulation of the interference pattern because of the irregular films between the silvered flats (A. M. Glauert, *Nature*, **168**, 861, 1951). Some new data are given here.

To simplify the conditions a thin cleaved sheet from a high-quality muscovite mica is used instead of a biological sample. It has been made quite clear already that such sheets can be cleaved of very uniform thickness (true to a molecular lattice) over considerable areas, but at the same time *they always wrinkle*. Thickness is unchanged, but hills and valleys appear and the hill on the one side has its complementary valley on the reverse. In addition it is crystalline and therefore birefringent.

The Fizeau fringe pattern given with unpolarized monochromatic light when a very thin mica sheet is pressed between silvered flats is shown in Plate 189 (× 50). This fringe pattern is most peculiar, for the sheet consists of strips of uniform thickness and uniform refractive index. Fringes appear in pairs. One pair can be markedly zig-zag, the other with one fringe zig-zag and the second straight or again both may be straight. The insertion of a suitably oriented polaroid as in Plate 190 (× 50) and Plate 191 (× 50) can cut out one or other of these patterns. They are therefore plane-polarized, mutually perpendicularly. The first point of importance is that neither of the polarized fringe patterns is giving obvious information about the *thickness or refractivity* of the sheet of mica. A simple experiment proves that the *wrinkling* is responsible for the complexity of the pattern.

In this experiment the following arrangement was used. A glass flat was silvered. A thin sheet of mica was silvered on the lower face, but only on the right-hand half, the left-hand half being unsilvered.

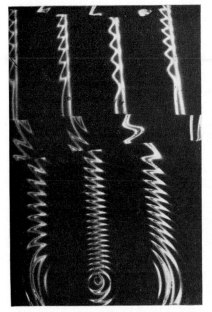

189

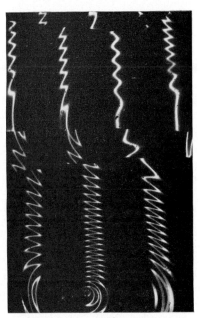

190

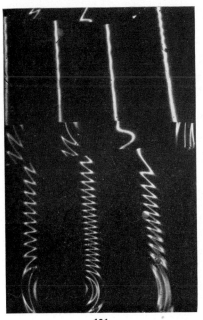

191

192

Plates 189-192

A glass flat was now silvered, but only the left-hand half was coated and this was placed on top of the mica. It is clear what the combination will do. On the left, is unsilvered mica between two silvered flats, and this will give the kind of complex fringe pattern under consideration, indeed of the kind like Plate 189. On the right half, on the contrary, is the ordinary arrangement for showing the topographical shape of the *mica surface*, and this will include both cleavage and the wrinkling shape. The compound fringe pattern secured is shown in Plate 192 (× 50). On the left is the double complex, on the right the ordinary topographical shape of the mica surface.

It can be seen very clearly that the zig-zag fringes are nothing more than parts of the continuation of the topographical surface wrinkling pattern, but doubled because of birefringence. The two patterns are intimately related. The theory of the formation of the complex on the left has been given by S. C. Hunter and F. R. N. Nabarro (*Phil. Mag.*, **43**, 538, 1952) in terms of a modulation of the interference pattern introduced by the wrinkling. The wrinkling leads to multiple-beam interference in a system in which a thin mica film of uniform thickness is situated between two air films of different thicknesses locally, but whose sum everywhere is constant. This triple film combination, the character of which determines the wrinkling, produces the modulation observed.

When the complexities of the separate regions of Plate 189 are considered in relation to the *known* uniformity in thickness in each region between cleavage lines, it is quite evident that any attempt to study a biological material by ' sandwiching ' it between silvered flats, will be fraught with the gravest of difficulties in interpretation. For it will be quite impossible to sort out the separate effects due to : (1) wrinkling ; (2) thickness changes ; (3) refractive index variations ; (4) birefringence ; and (5) differential absorption. The complex information lying latent in the interferogram is not amenable to interpretation so that such a method of investigation ought not to be attempted.

Although these patterns constitute an attractive academic exercise in optical analysis, they certainly do point to the danger inherent in attempting biological measurement by placing thin objects between silvered flats. This is not advised.

REFERENCE

No. 56.

PART FIVE

CRYSTAL OSCILLATORS

15. THE OSCILLATIONS OF QUARTZ CRYSTALS

The study of quartz crystal oscillators—Fracture—Studies on quartz clocks—A low-dispersion technique for discs—References.

The Study of Quartz Crystal Oscillators

ONE of the most attractive applications yet made with multiple-beam interferometry has been the study of the piezo-electric oscillations of quartz crystals. Such piezo-electric oscillators play a fundamental part in electronic frequency control and also as standard clocks of very high precision. There exists a formidably large literature on both the theory and the practice of the use of quartz oscillators. The electro-mechanical oscillation of a quartz oscillator depends both upon its shape and its cut, i.e. on the way in which it is sectioned from the quartz crystal. Variously, use has been made of thin rectangular plates, circular discs, rectangular bars or annular rings. Commonly, four distinct varieties of cut are used, three called X, Y, Z, which are plates perpendicular to the X, Y, Z directions in the crystal and a specifically inclined cut, called GT, selected for temperature stability.

Such crystals are usually excited into oscillation with a valve circuit by placing the crystal either between electrodes, or coating the surfaces with thin metal films and using these as electrodes. It is recognized that four types of motion may exist either separately or in combination, namely flexure, extension (or compression), shear and torsion. Coupling between some of these can often be expected and thus highly complex oscillatory amplitude distributions can be anticipated in these cases.

We realized that it might be possible to study both the distribution of nodes and antinodes and also the actual local amplitudes on the surfaces of oscillating quartz crystals by the use of multiple-beam interferometry. It was recognized at the outset that only vibrations in the up-down direction, i.e. perpendicular to the surface, would be registered, nevertheless the promise of a direct measurement of amplitudes was attractive.

In the event, the techniques we have developed have proved themselves to be of real value and offer considerable information. Dye (*Proc. Roy. Soc.*, A,138,1,1932) had already shown that two-beam inter-

ference could be used to examine quartz oscillations. This was in fact
not known in my laboratory when experiments were begun. Nevertheless, even so, it remained to be shown experimentally whether a
quartz vibrator would oscillate with sufficient stability in its nodal
pattern to give standing waves with so sensitive a system as a multiple-
beam interferometer. In the event it turned out that the stability was
remarkable indeed. Nodal regions can remain at rest to within say
50 Å, whilst neighbouring regions might be oscillating with an amplitude
of 5000 or even 10,000 Å. The multiple-beam systems are so superior
to two-beam systems that all earlier work such as that of Dye and of
Osterberg (*Proc. Nat. Acad. Sci.*, **15**, 892, 1929 and subsequently) which
used two-beam methods, has been far surpassed by the experiments now
to be described. Extensive experiments, some using polarized light
and others lycopodium powder, to simulate the classical Chladni plate
experiments, have been reported, but they do not offer the information
made available by transmission multiple-beam interferometry. For
instance, whilst lycopodium shows the nodal and antinodal regions, the
interference fringes show much finer detail and, what is far more important, give numerical data for the actual local amplitudes.

In all these experiments it has been necessary to use quartz oscillators
with surfaces reasonably well plane-polished. One surface is coated
with silver and this is either held close to or indeed rests on a silvered
optical flat. This constitutes one electrode, and a second electrode
either in ring form, a thin metal film, or a grid of wires, is placed suitably
on or near the other side of the crystal. The oscillations are induced
by orthodox Pierce or Hartley oscillator circuits of standard design.

The illumination for the fringe system was normally the usual mercury
arc, but stroboscopic experiments were also carried out with specially
designed light sources to be described later. The system was illuminated
to produce fringes of suitable dispersion. The oscillator was set into
action and at a variety of frequencies resonance could be induced leading
to oscillation fringe patterns. These stationary patterns remained perfectly steady for hours and it was easy to secure fringe pictures at low
magnifications in a matter of minutes.

One of the first successful pictures obtained is shown in Plate 193
(× 6) which was given by a rectangular cut GT crystal, dimensions
approximately 3 × 4 × 1 mm, cut for a fundamental frequency of
100 kc/s. The top electrode was a coarse wire grid, which throws a
shadow. The interference pattern shown was given at a frequency of
about 3 Mc/s. Numerous features are of interest. First it should be
recognized that the optical finish of the quartz crystal surface was

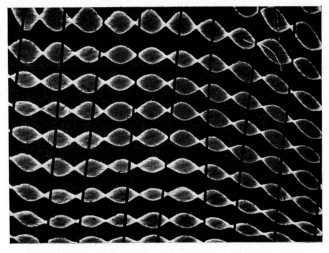

193

194

195

196

197

198

Plates 193-198

imperfect such that the fringes curve over instead of being in straight lines and the dispersion is variable.

The whole character of the vibration, which is a high order flexure, appears. There are a series of linear nodes running across the crystal, equally spaced. These nodal regions are very sharply delineated although they are not quite at rest. In terms of fractions of an order the amplitudes in successive regions between nodes are uniform and fill something like half an order. There is a noticeable irregularity near the top edge.

The fringe pattern shows only the up-down movements and no horizontal movements, if any, are revealed. The up-down movements are of the order of a quarter of a light wave and it can be expected that horizontal movements due to shear actions, Poisson's ratio effects and so on might well be of similar order. Such small displacements along the surface are only half the resolving power of an oil immersion high-power microscope objective, hence clearly such displacements are entirely unobservable on the low magnification pictures used in these experiments.

Of particular interest is the intensity distribution within the system. With a sinusoidal oscillation of the surface the velocity is least towards the ends of the oscillation (dropping to zero) and a maximum at the centre. As a consequence the fringe pattern shows a bright envelope, since the illumination times at the ends of the oscillation exceed those at the middle. This, it will be seen later, is most advantageous. The equality in intensity and narrowness of the envelopes is evidence that there is no drift in the fringes.

We shall consider first the application of this technique to a particular quartz bar with its length along the X-axis, of dimensions $56 \times 9 \times 9$ mm. The face normal to the Y-axis was polished and silvered and arrangements were made to direct the electric field either along the Y- or the X-axis, at will. With the field along the Y-axis, the odd modes were excited and when along the X-axis, the even flexural modes appeared. A succession of flexure modes is shown in Plates 194 to 198 (all at magnification $\times 1\frac{1}{2}$). Plate 194 shows the 4th mode, 195 the 5th, 196 the 6th, 197 the 7th, 198 the 8th mode. The modes are recognizable by the increase in the number of nodes.

There are several points of interest on the interferogram of Plate 198. It can be seen that the amplitude varies along the bar. Again, some amplitudes extend over more than two complete orders, yet there is no real confusion. This is attributable to the advantageous envelope intensity distribution to which attention was drawn in Plate 193.

199

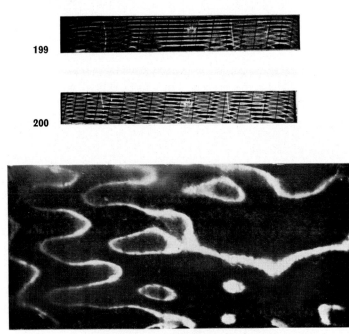

200

201

202

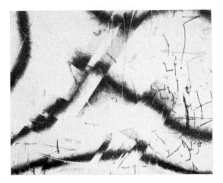

203

Plates 199-203

M_2

Despite overlap, exact amplitude measurement is possible. The frequencies required to excite the patterns on Plates 194 to 198 form an approximate harmonic series.

At selected frequencies either simple longitudinal modes or complex combinations of longitudinal and flexure modes can be excited. The complexity typical of two such selected combinations is demonstrated by Plates 199 (× 1½) and 200 (× 1½). The variations of nodes and antinodes are clearly shown.

It will be recognized that whilst these oscillation interferograms give information about local *amplitudes*, they give no information at all as to local *phase*. It is not known which parts at any time are going up when other parts are going down. To reveal such a phase it is necessary to use some stroboscopic illumination which is certainly difficult as the experiments are conducted in a high-frequency range. We succeeded in obtaining a good stroboscope condition in two ways. In the first method a high-frequency electrodeless discharge was excited in a low-pressure mercury vapour capillary tube. A coupling circuit was arranged to tap off volts from the oscillator circuit driving the crystal and this produced one flash per cycle. A capillary tube source proved workable up to 1 Mc/s and no doubt the de-ionization needed for rapid quenching was assisted by the capillary walls.

The fringe system was therefore produced with a mercury source flashing at the same frequency as the oscillating crystal itself and thus a stroboscope pattern of fringes was obtainable.

Beyond 1 Mc/s a Kerr cell and polarized light were used, the cell being driven by a fraction of the crystal driving-voltage tapped off from the crystal oscillator circuit. Certain electronic difficulties were encountered but were in due course overcome. A normal interferometric light source can be employed with the Kerr cell.

Plate 201 (× 7) is an example of a stroboscopic fringe picture at 650 kilocycle frequency given by a quartz plate and using the high-frequency electrodeless source. This shows in a very striking way the phase relations on the surface. It is easy to bias the system to move to a different part of the cycle. There is a very high degree of stroboscopic illumination considering the great frequency.

Fracture

It is well known that quartz crystals can easily be shattered if overdriven and we have made some useful interferometric observations in this connection. One bar which had been very crudely polished and was appreciably cylindrical was found after excitation to reveal discrete slip-steps on the surface. An interferogram using three radiations (green and two yellow lines) is shown in Plate 202 ($\times$ 4). The slip-steps are indicated at the right. Plate 203 ($\times$ 25) shows part of the slip region, with green light only. There are two sets of steps, inclined respectively at some 35° and 50° to the direction of the Z-axis. Step heights are of the order of 500 Å, and are fairly uniform in value. We find that when such bars are over-excited until they fracture, *they do in fact fracture along these very slip-step directions.* Clearly we have here, by accident, caught a case at the early stage before incipient fracture has set in and it is equally clear that the effect is strictly crystallographic, almost in the nature of a typical crystal cleavage.

It may well be that we have here a clue to the well-known ageing effect of quartz clocks and quartz oscillators. A very small change in physical dimensions or in elastic properties is needed, perhaps a few parts in 10^8, to affect the crystal sufficiently. The back of the crystal also shows dimensional changes so that the slip-step effectively modifies the dimensions, and so the frequency.

Studies on Quartz Clocks

In 1938 Essen, at the National Physical Laboratory, designed what has since become a standard quartz clock oscillator of very high precision. This is in the form of a hollow annular ring with axis in the Z-direction and with the electric axes in the plane of the ring. It is designed to be oscillated in longitudinal compression. An alternating field is applied to coaxial ring electrodes with the intention of producing circumferential strains of opposite sign, 60° apart. Theory shows that the lower frequency should have nodes at the six regions where the planes containing the Z-axis and the three X-axes cut the ring. The ring is thereupon supported at three of these nodes.

Dr. Essen kindly loaned three of his ring clocks of frequencies approximating to 100 and 200 kc/s. The rings were well polished and the annular surface was silvered and matched against a silvered flat. Adjustment of dispersion offered difficulties but these were overcome.

Two interferograms are shown, in Plate 204 ($\times$ 2) and Plate 205 ($\times$ 2). In Plate 204 there is a 12-fold symmetry and in Plate 205 an 18-fold symmetry. It was established by supporting the rings on ball-bearings, set at 20° around a circle, that the position of the ring on the bearings is not responsible for the observed unexpected high multiplicity of nodes.

It has been found that whole ranges of nodal patterns with nodes of from 4 to 18 can be excited, each pattern associated with its own

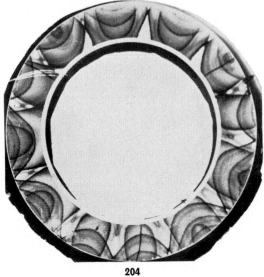

204

205

Plates 204, 205

frequency. For any one ring the succession of nodes occur at frequencies which are more or less in harmonic progression with the number.

Far more complex patterns involving combinations of vibrational type are observed at higher frequencies. We have established on one Essen ring that there are twelve nodal regions and twelve antinodal regions. The nodes are of two quite distinct sets. Three pairs appear at the ends of three diameters and three pairs between these, but lying on radii which are not quite colinear, i.e. not diametrally.

With a standard clock the amplitude appears to be linearly proportional to the crystal current. In one particular arrangement each total excursion of amplitude of 100 Å was produced by radio frequency current of some 3 mA. The measurements were taken up to a crystal current of 7 mA.

A Low-Dispersion Technique for Discs

We have extended considerably our study on quartz discs by deliberately adopting a modified low-dispersion technique. When ordinary high-dispersion fringes are used there is always the very real possibility of missing nodal regions, but this is not so when a large number of fringes covers the field of view. Studies were made with discs of 1-in. diameter and of varying thickness. When experiments were made on Z-cut discs, in order to avoid the possibility of short-circuit, it was advantageous to replace the conducting silver coatings with insulating dielectric multilayers. At times as many as 100 fringes crossing the 1-in. field of view have been used. This leads to considerable fringe broadening, as has already been established, yet there is a resultant gain despite fringe broadening.

Longitudinal vibrations in a circular Z-cut quartz disc can occur in a variety of ways predicted by elastic theory. Displacement types can be either radial (A), tangential (B) or combined radial and tangential (C). Each can occur in a succession of modes ($m = 1, 2, 3$, etc.). We have succeeded in studying a complex range of such oscillations, the observed pattern depending markedly on the thickness of the disc.

Plate 206 ($\times$ 3) shows a radial oscillation of type A for a 1-mm thick crystal whilst on the contrary Plate 207 ($\times$ 3) shows the corresponding pattern for a 2-mm thick crystal.

These interferograms show in a notable fashion the distributions of vibration of nodes and antinodes. The dark regions where there is no fringe broadening are antinodal. In a sense we have a ' Chladni-plate ' pattern, with the added advantage that the local fringe broadening reveals the amplitude.

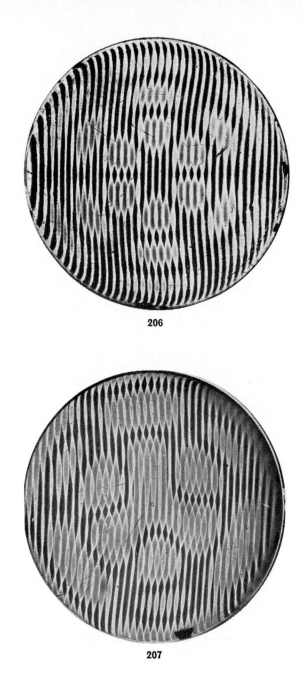

206

207

Plates 206, 207

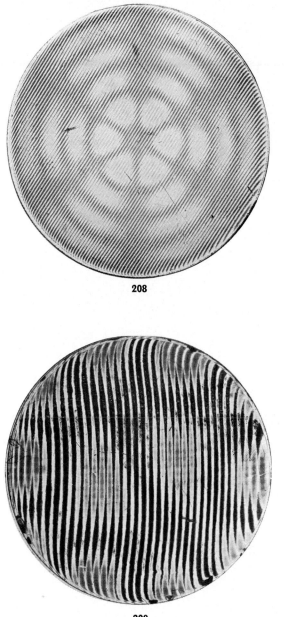

208

209

Plates, 208, 209

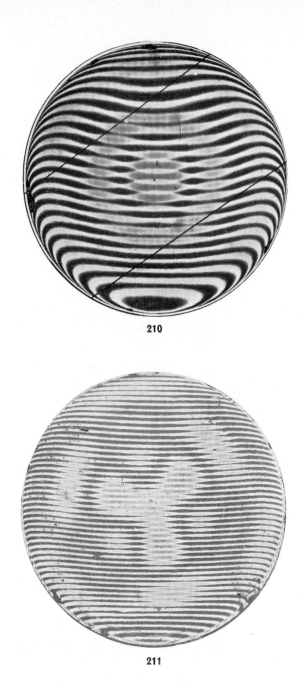

210

211

Plates 210, 211

An isotropic disc vibrating in B mode, having true tangential vibration, should display no interferometric pattern since there is theoretically no motion up and down, but we find experimentally this is far from the case. Plate 208 (× 3) is an example in which the frequency of vibration corresponds to a B-type mode, yet the pattern is flexural in behaviour.

Plate 209 (× 3) is a C-type excitation and is clearly of a complex character.

However, this interferometric approach to the study of quartz vibrations can offer still further information. With a thin disc polished on both sides and a suitable wedge angle adopted, it is possible to secure broad fringes *through* the crystal. Such fringes, when the crystal oscillates, can now show effects due both to change of thickness and of refractive index. There can therefore be distinct birefringent doubling. Owing to the interferometrically large separation of the surfaces (1 mm), fringe definition is very poor indeed ; nevertheless useful interferograms can be secured.

In type-A modes the shear stress is theoretically small so that fringe splitting is not expected to be noticeable with the poor fringe definition available. Any observed fringe displacement will be due to dilational stress. A type A, $m = 2$, mode fringe pattern taken *through* the crystal is shown in Plate 210 (× 3).

In type B oscillations should be zero and the shear stress should be responsible for the pattern. Yet Plate 210, which refers to type B, shows distinct evidence of birefringent fringe splitting, proving the existence of considerable dilational stress also. Clearly much is to be learnt from such interferograms.

Plate 211 (× 3) is selected as a further example of a complex vibration. The cases chosen here are merely representative but sufficient has been shown to illustrate that the interferometric method has much to offer when associated with frequency measurements concerning the study of quartz oscillators. Oscillation phenomena can be highly complex, yet the complexity is simplified by the very restrictions of the fringe broadening to the up-down direction.

REFERENCES

Nos. 20, 32, E, 55, R.

PART SIX

STUDIES OF SURFACE DEFORMATIONS
METALS
INDENTATIONS ON METALS
PERCUSSION OF DIAMOND

16. SOME STUDIES ON METALS

Slip phenomena—Slip on titanium crystals—Etching of germanium crystals—Machined metals—Diamond-turned aluminium surfaces—Superfine grinding on steel—Edge of a razor blade—Contouring in electrodeposition—References.

THIS section will be concerned with a number of unrelated studies on metal surfaces. The main object is to show that multiple-beam interferometry can materially assist both in metallurgical examination of metals and in technological examination of engineering surfaces. No attempt is made at any detailed discussion of the observations, the prime object being to illustrate potential applications. More attention will be paid later to the study of the surface deformations associated with the indentations made for testing the hardness of metals. In this field multiple-beam interferometry has already made a substantial contribution, and this will be reviewed later.

Slip Phenomena

The study of slip in crystals is considered nowadays of much importance. Interferometry can, in suitable cases, offer information. Slip effects have been noticed in many of our hardness indentation studies on many non-metallic crystals. For example, Plate 212 (× 100) shows the interference pattern of a beautiful slip effect found on a diamond. In this, a succession of growth steps run from north-west to south-east, crossed in the middle by the horizontal slip line, at which fringe displacement appears.

It is, however, on metal crystals that slip effects are most readily observed. Thus an aluminium crystal which had been subject to tension produced the slip pattern shown in Plate 213 (× 70). The poor quality of the crystal's surface is responsible for the imperfect fringes. Another region on the same crystal in Plate 214 (× 170) shows up the stepped character of the slip. This slip is on a relatively coarse scale in extension and it is well known that the electron microscope often reveals that each kind of slip shown here is actually a complex of many close steps. That this is so is also recognizable also from the slight slope of the ' riser ' on the staircase. It is an unresolved staircase itself.

183

212

213

214

Plates 212-214

Titanium Crystals

A particularly interesting set of effects has been found on strained titanium crystals. Plate 215 ($\times$ 100) shows the interferogram obtained by stretching a single-crystal of Ti. There is both a coarse and a fine structure (see also Plate 122). Another interferogram is shown in Plate 216 ($\times$ 270) and attention is drawn to this for several reasons. Careful observation will reveal that some fine structure is repeated in a succession of fringes, one above the other. This shows that there are very shallow slip lines in the pattern. However, these titanium pictures are of particular optical interest in that they were obtained with two special techniques, with microflats and with multilayers, for the crystal surface was so irregular that only the conical micro-flat technique could be used. Then, again, titanium has quite a high inherent natural reflectivity and it was decided not to silver, and a seven-layer multilayer was selected for the matching flat. As seen from the two plates very intense contrast was obtained in the fringe pattern as a result of this.

Etched Germanium

Germanium crystals play an important part today in semi-conductor researches. It is possible by special methods to grow single crystals of germanium with a natural smooth surface (see, for example, Plates 103 and 104). The majority of the semi-conductor studies are made with germanium plates which are first ground flat and then etched. The surface of an etched crystal has been studied here interferometrically. The crystal was first ground with 600 mesh Carborundum powder and then etched in the germanium etchant known as CP_4.

An interferogram of such a surface is shown in Plate 217 ($\times$ 350). To obtain this, only a thin silvering on the matching flat was used because the natural germanium surface itself (unsilvered) was being examined. The two reflectivities are not very high. Although contrast is good, the fringes are accompanied by faint ghost effects, but these do not detract from the analysis of the topography. The etch pits are deep round hollows, not quite circular, and there seems some evidence of orientation in the directions of the cliptical axes. Interference between the pits has clearly taken place, but on the whole there is a slight orientation effect.

Machined Metals

Within recent years considerable attention has been paid to the perfection of industrial engineering high-precision grinding and honing

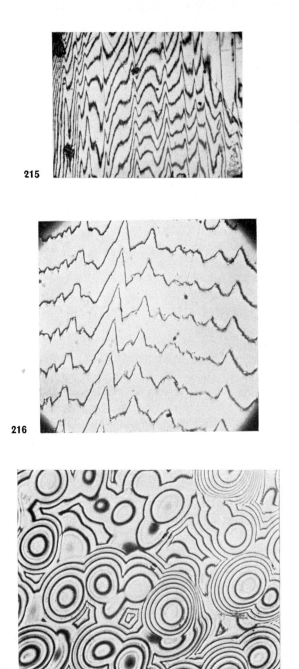

215

216

217

Plates 215-217

operations for metal products, especially for machine components. The assessment of metal finish by a variety of engineering processes has become important. Generally speaking fine finishes can be secured by turning with diamond cutting tools, by broaching, or by superfine grinding. As a rule polishing processes are too costly for industry although electro-polish has found many applications. Broadly, three methods have been developed for assessment of finish of industrial products. There are, first, stylus methods in which a hard diamond or sapphire tip is trailed over the surface. Like the old phonograph stylus, it records the surface pattern. The movement is electrically amplified and either a current record or a pen record gives a line profile of the surface. There are two drawbacks : (1) only a narrow line section is surveyed ; (2) if the surface is very soft (and this can happen, in for instance an automobile shell bearing) the testing diamond stylus *ploughs through the hills and dales* (it leaves a visible scratch) and records a false smoother value than it should do. Stylus methods are widely used for *hard* materials and are safe in such cases.

The second method, which is not as yet extensively employed, is the pneumatic gauge. A fine jet of air impinges on the surface (the nozzle being close to that surface) which is trailed past the jet (or vice versa). As the distance between jet and surface varies the pressure at the orifice changes and a pen record of this can be converted into the height changes. The method is mechanically difficult and again it gives only a line profile (averaged over the width of the nozzle). It has obvious limitations, but is non-destructive.

A third and comprehensive method of examining surface finish is by interferometry, both two-beam and multiple-beam. If both very high lateral magnification and high lateral resolution are required, then two-beam interferometry always enables full optical resolution of a microscope to be used in all cases, but at the expense of a reduced sensitivity in depth. Very many machine processes do not justify the use of maximum resolution in extension, yet still require high resolution in depth. Such cases are best studied with multiple-beam interference and in this section three selected examples will be illustrated, showing what the technique has to offer.

Diamond-Turned Bearings

Plate 218 (× 170) shows the interference pattern given by a soft tin-aluminium alloy cylindrical bearing. This had been turned by a diamond lathe-cutting tool and was inherently far too soft to tolerate a diamond stylus examination. The successive tool cuts are clearly shown to be

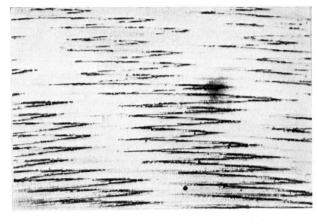

218

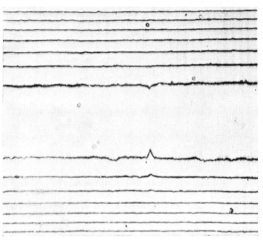

219

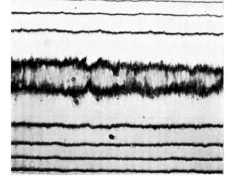

220

Plates 218-220

in the form of a regular succession of valleys, perhaps 2000 Å deep, with appreciable variation in depth. It will be noticed that not only does the zig-zag fringe pattern give effectively a profile, but in addition the interferogram *reveals the topography of a whole area*, which is what the stylus methods fail to do.

Superfine Grinding on Steel

Plate 219 (× 140) shows the admirable finish obtainable on a steel rod by modern super-grinding methods, without subsequent polishing. Since the object is a cylinder, the fringe pattern consists of cylindrical Newton's ' rings '. Fringe definition is, as one expects, only at its best near the central orders. The interferogram shows one scratch or rut, but otherwise the surface structure is surprisingly good. Plate 220 (× 140) shows another picture on the same cylinder taken with a central high-dispersion fringe, which shows up the circular grinding marks more easily. The interferograms show that superfine grinding methods give remarkably good finishes.

The very real advantage of an interferogram over a line section is clear, especially in Plate 219. The probability of a stylus trail striking the individual scratch on this picture is very remote. The interferogram gives on the other hand a comprehensive survey in extension. On this particular picture dispersion in the first pair of fringes is such that magnification is of the order of 40,000 times which is adequate for most purposes. In Plate 220, in the central fringe, the magnification is much higher and the micro-structure is revealed. The technologist is usually satisfied with pictures of this type.

Edge of a Razor Blade

Amongst good machine finishes are the cutting edges of safety razor blades. An examination has been made of the region near a blade edge. An interferogram is shown in Plates 221 and 222 (× 350). The top of Plate 222 is a continuation of the bottom of Plate 221. The edge is at the right-hand side and the region shown is 1 mm in length on the blade. A width of 0·06 mm from the edge is illustrated.

There is a good deal of information on such an interferogram. The region shown has cylindrical concave curvature. The character of the machining is well revealed here. The fringes, which run up to the edge itself, show serrations up to perhaps 1/5th of an order, say 500 Å. In addition there are two distinct wave patterns : one in which the fringes run into the edge at intervals of about $\frac{3}{4}$ mm and within these are secondary loops at rough intervals of perhaps a fifth of this.

221   222

Plates 221, 222

The fringes were obtained by selecting a suitable multilayer to match the reasonably good reflectivity of the steel itself, hence the good contrast.

Contouring of Electrodeposition

During some studies on the hardness of electrodeposited alloys questions arose concerning the efficiency of contour in electrodeposition. Electroplaters have long been familiar with two distinctive properties of various plating solutions. Some have what is called good throwing power, and in these cases deposited metal is thrown into hollow regions, producing better and more uniform deposits than one would anticipate from the simple field-current distribution due to electrode shape. This is on a macro-scale, involving dimensions up to some centimetres.

Another type of contouring with which the plater is familiar is on a micro-scale effect. Two kinds of electroplates are known, those with and those without a ' *smoothing* ' action. In a deposit with a smoothing action there is *preferential build up* within scratches and depressions and the final electroplated surface is smoother and less free from scattering scratches than the original. Clearly this is technically of value since the final polish on a prepared piece of work is improved by the plating, and therefore less care is needed in the pre-polish before plating ; and this pre-polish is a major cost item in preparing materials for a bright finish. There are, on the other hand, some electroplates which do not smooth out scratches. They are those with the good theoretical contouring properties. A scratch at the beginning is retained, and such electroplates are not valued industrially if a bright finish is required. Electroplates in industry have usually two purposes, either (*a*) protective, or (*b*) aesthetic appearance. An efficient contouring protective film is adequate in the many industrial finishes which are not concerned with appearance.

In our experiments on the hardness of an electroplated alloy an electrodeposited tin-nickel alloy was selected. This is very hard (Vickers hardness about 700), but the prime reason for selecting this was the fact that a process has become available (developed at the Tin Research Institute) whereby this alloy can be electrodeposited very bright, with a natural high reflectivity of over 80%. This makes the material ideal for thin-film deposition studies. Most other electrodeposits require polishing or burnishing after deposition and clearly such a mechanical action deforms and work-hardens the very film under study. This is a serious matter if hardness is being studied. In contour efficiency studies, any after-polishing process, following deposition, would be disastrous and invalidate the whole investigation because of flow and smearing effects due to polishing.

Bright tin-nickel alloy has 65% Sn and 35% Ni and probably has the structure SnNi. It is deposited under critical conditions from a solution of $SnCl_2$ and $NiCl_2$ to which has been added $NH_4F.HF$ and NH_4OH. The temperature must exceed 70° C and the pH is critical, about 2·5. The electrolyte is highly corrosive, but some plastics and rubbers are quite resistant. The electrodeposited alloy has remarkable resistance to tarnish. Experience shows that if it is deposited on a smooth surface it emerges bright from the plating bath, but if deposited on a rough or matt surface, it emerges matt, but can be polished up. This is an indication that we have here a good contouring deposit (good in the scientific sense, not in the industrial sense).

The film thicknesses found desirable in industrial practice range from 7·5 microns to 25 microns, the thinner films being decorative and tarnish-resisting whilst the thicker are in addition wear-resisting. What was required for a specific technological purpose was some indication of contour efficiency somewhere within this thickness range. It was decided to deposit over the edge of a step of some 4 microns in height a succession of electrodeposits of thickness 2 to 14 microns, the height of the edge to be studied with interferometry, after each deposition. A sharp suitable step could not easily be obtained, and after trials involving scratches, etc., finally the following was adopted.

A brass plate was polished and then plated with a thin bright coating of tin-nickel. The plate was immersed half-way in Formvar solution, lifted out to drain and dry and then replated to a thickness of about 4 microns. The Formvar was removed, leaving a step. An interferogram is shown in Plate 223 (× 25).

In this, the upper half was that coated with Formvar and the lower half that which received the additional deposit. Although the Formvar edge is sharp the deposit drops down regularly over about a millimetre on the metal surface.

From the fringes of equal chromatic order, Plate 224 (× 45), the difference in height over the step is found to be 4·29 micron. These also show which is the up and which the down region.

When a film of about 2 micron in thickness is deposited on the step the fringe pattern obtained is that in Plate 225 (× 45). The measured step, avoiding the region of curved fringes, i.e. away from the obvious irregularity, is now 4·21 micron which is not effectively different. With 6-, 10- and 14-micron thick films, the fringe patterns obtained are those shown in Plate 226 (× 45), Plate 227 (× 45) and Plate 228 (× 45).

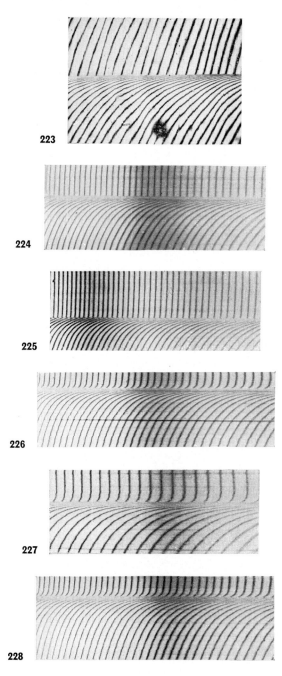

Plates 223-228

The important feature in all three interferograms is the onset of a curvature at the foot of the straight fringes in the *upper half* of the field of view.

The upper set of fringes which ran initially straight up to the edge now all curl towards the red end of the spectrum. This indicates that there is failure to deposit here near the edge itself. The drop at the edge amounts to some 0·1 micron for the 6-micron thickness of electrodeposit and increase to 0·18 micron for the 14-micron deposit.

Thus it is clear now that any existing scratches and defects, instead of being filled in, are actually accentuated by this particular electro-deposit. Hence to secure a bright scratch-free finish a smooth original surface is required.

REFERENCES

Nos. 27, D, S.

17. INDENTATION HARDNESS-TESTING OF METALS

Indentation hardness of isotropic materials—Micro-indents on polished homogeneous metals—Recovery in spherical indents—Volume of flow pattern—Exploitation of chromaticity of a multilayer—References.

Indentation Hardness of Isotropic Materials

THE resistance offered by a material to penetration by a rounded, conical or pyramidal indenter has long been used as a measure of hardness. A variety of hardness numbers is in use. Thus in the Brinell hardness, introduced in 1900, a hard spherical indenter is pressed into the surface under study (most frequently a metal). The load is applied slowly and maintained for a standard time (30 seconds). A permanent indent is made and its diameter measured. The Brinell hardness number (B.H.N.) is computed as the ratio of applied load W to surface area of the indent and is easily obtained by measuring the diameter D of the ball and the diameter d of the cup-like depression. It is not too satisfactory a measure, for the load-bearing area varies with the applied load. A better measure is the Meyer hardness number (M.H.N. 1908) which adopts the mean pressure as the hardness figure. Meyer found empirically that the load W is related to the diameter d by a law $W = ad^n$ in which the Meyer index n varies from about 2·5 for annealed metals to 2·0 for work-hardened metals.

Following Ludwik (1908), the widely used Rockwell test was then developed. An indenting cone is attached to a highly sensitive dial which registers the penetration. A small fixed load is applied and the penetration depth noted. Then a larger standard load is applied. This extra load is removed and the subsequent measure is the additional depth (after elastic recovery) produced by the additional load.

Smith and Sandland (1922) then introduced the now popular Vickers pyramid diamond indenter and this diamond pyramid hardness (HV) vies with the Rockwell in practical use. When using a ball impression with ball of diameter D it is found advantageous to produce values of d lying between the range $\frac{1}{4}D$ to $\frac{1}{2}D$. Taking $\frac{3}{8}D$ as a mean, the tangents drawn to a circle at the ends of a chord of length $\frac{3}{8}D$ in a circle of diameter D include an angle of $136°$. This then is chosen for convenience as the angle of the Vickers pyramid. It is a pyramid on a square base with included angle $136°$ between opposite pairs of faces. The HV is defined as the load per unit bearing area and is measured by

$$HV = \frac{2W \sin \theta/2}{d^2}$$ in which θ is $136°$ and d is the diagonal of the indenta-

tion in mm, W is kg. Because the indentations with different loads are geometrically similar the hardness computed should be independent of the applied load. A considerable advantage of this is the possibility of micro-tests with a very sharp diamond pyramid.

Now there are three reasons why interferometry can be successfully applied to the study of micro-indentation. First the phenomena of surface flow can be examined, second there are questions of recovery and third studies on the indenting tools themselves. It has long been known, from micro-indentation studies, that the indentation shape made by a square-based pyramid is not always a perfect square, nor does the region surrounding the indent remain flat. It is generally considered that if the capacity of the metal for work-hardening is low, then the metal displaced by the indenter flows up the faces of the indenting tool, rising most at the centre. This has two consequences, first the square-shape converts into a barrel-shape outline, second the excess material is piled up at the edges.

An annealed material, which has a high capacity for cold working, tends to be pushed away outward from the indenter. The result in this case is that the metal edge sinks lower near the centre of the square face which leads to a ' pin-cushion ' shape, with what is called ' sinking-in '. Even with sinking-in, there is a pile-up some distance beyond the edge. It is clearly evident that interferometry is an ideal approach to the study of pile-up and sink-in effects.

There are two types of recovery effect which can be studied interferometrically. Thus, for example, in a Brinell indent, when the ball is removed there will be an elastic recovery *within* the indent and the curvature will change, the indent becoming less deep than it should be. For micro-indents with small load this elastic effect becomes progressively more serious the smaller the indent. For small loads false hardness numbers will be computed. It will be shown how the small recovery can be determined interferometrically. A study of the actual shape of the indenting tools has not received the attention it deserves and it will be shown later that interferometry has something to offer here. Finally there are available excellent micro-indenting machines which can be mounted on microscopes and with small loads satisfactory micro-indents can be accurately placed on small specimens

Micro-indents on Polished Homogeneous Metals

The polish obtainable on a metallic specimen is a variable matter. Multiple-phase alloys can consist of regions of different hardness and this can lead to irregularity in the polish. Plate 229 ($\times$ 60) is an interferogram of the typical kind of polish secured on a steel (exceptional steels can give better surfaces). In these studies steel will be regarded as a homogeneous material, since the microstructure is so much smaller than the indents made.

Plate 230 ($\times$ 80) shows the interferogram of the region surrounding an indent made on steel with a pyramid. The load is 5 kg. Plate 231 ($\times$ 80) was made with 15 kg and Plate 232 ($\times$ 80) with 40 kg. The following features emerge :

(1) The fringes reveal a pile-up which in each case is a maximum opposite the face centre. (It is easily established that these are hillocks, not valleys.)

(2) There is relatively little surface distortion along the extension of the diagonals. Traditionally the diagonals of the indents are measured and averaged. The interferograms prove this to be sound practice, for the surface distortion is a minimum along diagonal directions.

(3) Elastic recovery is shown by two features. Thus in an enlarged 5 kg picture (Plate 233 ($\times$ 230)) a pin-cushion effect is clear. Further the fringes dip in towards the edge, showing there is the local sink-in resulting from recovery. Proportionately the pin-cushion effect is greater in the smaller indent, as indeed elastic recovery should be. Plots of the profiles of the three indents show them to be very similar in shape and only to differ in scale. The 40 kg pattern has hillocks 6 light waves high, i.e. some 3 microns.

It is of considerable interest to note here that these interferograms confirm the validity of the recommendation of the British Standards Institute that micro-indents on a homogeneous material will not interfere with each other as *long as they are separated by at least* 2½ *times the length of the diagonal*. The effective distortion appears to spread by an amount which is about the length of a diagonal so that interference between two indents more than 2½ diagonals apart will be very slight. Emphasis is laid on the fact that it will later be established that this safety criterion cannot apply to indents made on single crystals.

The complete absence of a local sink-in appears for pyramid indents made on duraluminium, the interferogram of a 5 kg indent being shown

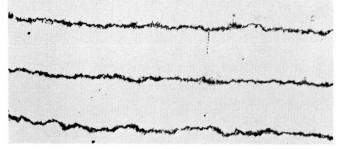

229

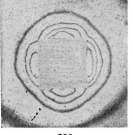

230

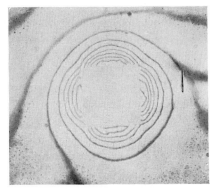

231

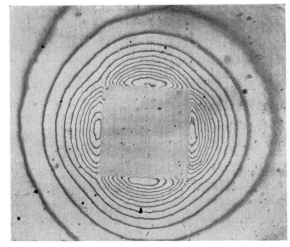

232

Plates 229-232

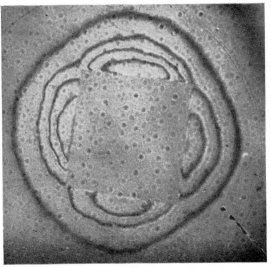

233

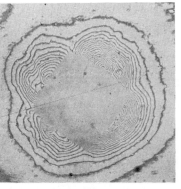

234

Plates 233, 234

in Plate 234 ($\times$ 80). The pile-up is very irregular and is considerable (12 light waves) but the fringes start straight from the edges of the indent.

On this indent the surface flow piles-up in an irregular fashion and we were inclined to blame the material. But a check was made with two-beam fringes on the state of polish of the four faces of the pyramid. The interferograms of the four faces are mounted together in Plate 235 ($\times$ 80). The faces are sufficiently plane to a length of 0·5 mm from the apex, indicating that a satisfactory indent up to a side length of 0·5 mm should be obtainable. Yet on the other hand only two faces are well polished and the polish on one is particularly ragged. We believe that this led to differential dragging. The observations indicated desirability for a re-polish and it is satisfactory to report that after re-polish much more symmetrical interferograms of indents were obtained. We advise that for high precision micro-indentation studies special interferometric attention should always be given to the polish of the indenter.

Recovery in Spherical Indents

The sphericity of a ball indenter is easily established by measuring the multiple-beam Newton's rings and plotting the order against the squares of the diameters. A good spherical surface gives a straight line. The topography of a selected 6 mm Hoffman ball-bearing steel sphere is shown by the interferogram in Plate 236 ($\times$ 170). The ball is of excellent quality with only slight local irregularities and this is generally true of all the balls *selected* for our experiments. Having established that the indenter is spherical, if now the fringes within an indentation do not correspond, this indicates the existence of a recovery shallowing effect.

Plate 237 ($\times$ 270) shows with high magnification a very shallow indent whose depth is only about 1/100th of the diameter. The plot of ring order number n against the square of the diameter d^2 shows marked deviation from a straight line. Had the indent remained really spherical a straight line would have been obtained. The d^2 value increases with n hence the higher order regions, which are the least depressed, are flatter than they should be, in other words the least depressed regions recover the most. This is exactly what one would expect, since for a sufficiently slight depression the distortion is mainly *elastic*, not plastic, and so effectively completely recovers.

Volume of Flow Pattern

We have carried out experiments with a ball indenter to attempt to

Plate 235

assess the relative volumes of the indentation and the metal forced up into the flow pattern.

The volume V of the depression can be derived from the diameter of the ball and the diameter of the indent. The volume in the flow pattern is obtainable directly from an interferogram such as Plate 238 ($\times$ 75). For with a spherical indenter we get a symmetrical flow which is very easily evaluated in section and by integration the volume displaced, v, is readily computed. Thus the volume displaced, as a fraction of the hole made, can now be assessed and we will call v/V the flow factor. It is clear that if there are no density changes then v/V will be unity, but if there is some compression under the load one can expect v/V to be less than one.

We have established that in practice v/V is often *less* than unity. In copper (HV = 98) it increased from 0·02 to 0·4 as the load increased. In a metal alloy of HV = 300 it increased from 0·14 to 0·24 with increased load and in a hard metal alloy (HV = 420) it was about 0·1. When account is taken of the region theoretically expected to be affected by the distortion, it appears that a change in density of some 0·2% can account for the material missing in the pile-up.

The true profile associated with pile-up is admirably shown in Plate 239 ($\times$ 80). This shows the interferogram for an indent made with a 1-mm ball. There are numerous close-packed fringes *within* the indent and a well-defined pile-up surrounding it. On Plate 240 ($\times$ 420) is a high-magnification picture which shows fringes of equal chromatic order over the edge region. It is seen that the pile-up does not begin at the edge, but that there is an abrupt local sink-in here. (Fringes are turned through 90° to show the direction of the profile section.)

Now it has already been pointed out that shallowing and recovery are most marked when the indentation is small, so that it can be expected that very shallow indents with light loads will have very small flow factors. The multiple-beam Fizeau fringes are not as well suited to show depressions of the order of half a light wave or less. For this purpose fringes of equal chromatic order are ideal. In Plate 241 ($\times$ 180) is shown the fringe system passing over a very shallow indentation. Its depth is just a little more than half a light wave. This is a diametral profile and it is seen that there is no measurable pile-up at all. The flow factor does indeed approximate to zero.

It should be recalled throughout this discussion that in these interferograms we are concerned with topographies on two very markedly different scales. The vertical scale can be 500 times the horizontal. For example a shallow indent is shown in Plate 242 with linear magnification

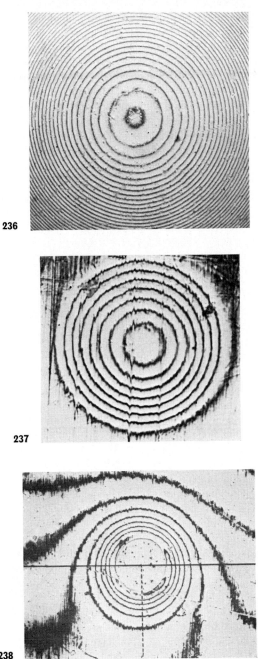

236

237

238

Plates 236-238

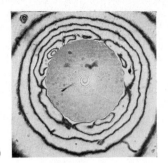

239

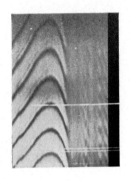

240

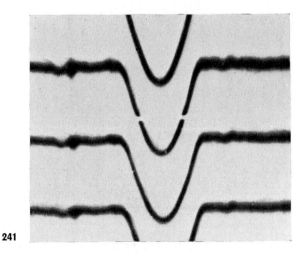

241

Plates 239-241

$\times$ 50. But the magnification in the fringe pattern is effectively 25,000 times.

As a result the profile pattern selected across the horizontal ink line drawn across the picture, and as shown below, appears on a scale such that the vertical magnification is 500 times that of the horizontal. This enormous vertical magnification must be borne in mind when considering the flow patterns. The effects are in reality on a much more micro-scale than they appear to be here.

Exploitation of Chromaticity of a Multilayer

Attention has been drawn before to the very real advantages possessed by dielectric multilayers as reflectors when viewing reflection fringes. They have an additional property which we have exploited, namely the sharply localized chromaticity of the reflectivity. If a multilayer is well designed to give a reflectivity of say 94% for the green mercury line, it is found experimentally that this falls off to perhaps 15% in the visible red. This two-fold reflectivity can be used in an interesting manner as shown in Plate 243 ($\times$ 40) and Plate 244 ($\times$ 40). Circular and pyramidal indentations were made on rolled polished brass, which actually reveal some marked directional properties. A 5-film multilayer has a reflectivity suitable for matching against polished brass. Reflection fringes were produced with a *white light* source, filtered with a green mercury filter, and are shown in Plate 243. For a non-monochromatic source the definition is excellent and this is primarily due to the selective action of the multilayer which picks out and multiply reflects its own peak wavelength.

Now one of the accepted drawbacks in reflection multiple-beam interferometry is that the total back-reflected light from the matching flat which overlays the object is such that one cannot see a micro-picture of the surface. One sees, it is true, the contouring by the fringes but not the actual surface itself ; it is obliterated by the reflected light. A separate micrograph is usually needed and to do this with silvered plates the interference system requires to be dismantled and the matching silvered flat removed.

Now it is just in this very connection where the chromaticity of the multilayer can be exploited. For with such a reflector it is not necessary to dismantle. All that is required is to remove the green filter and replace it by a red filter. In effect the multilayer has now become reasonably transparent. No fringes are produced and we see through it and secure a micrograph of the surface. Thus whilst Plate 243 was taken with green light, a mere change to a red filter and with no other

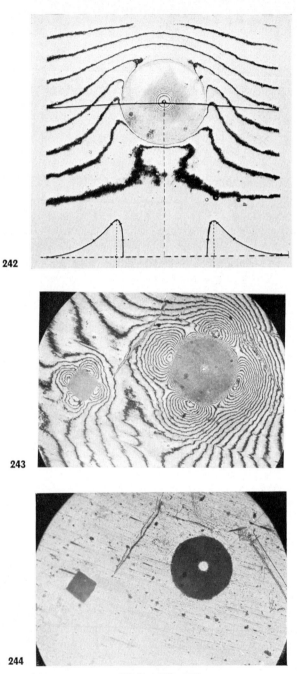

242

243

244

Plates 242-244

alteration, gives us Plate 244. Here a variety of cracks and scratches are now visible, all of which exactly correlate with fringe displacement patterns. Thus interpretation is materially assisted by this simple device.

REFERENCES

Nos. 25, 35, N, P, S, X.

18. INDENTATIONS ON SINGLE CRYSTALS

Tin—Directional studies with double cone indenter—References.

INTERFEROMETRIC studies of indentations made on single crystals have assisted materially in revealing differential hardness effects associated with the crystallographic symmetry. The first experiments we conducted were made on single crystals of tin. Tin was selected for several reasons. Its natural reflectivity is high (some 85%) and it is easy to obtain reasonably large single crystals, or at least isolated single crystallites within a larger melt. It melts at a low temperature (232° C) and, finally, its hardness is so low that only loads of a few grams need be applied to the indenting machine. Thus the precision micro-indenting machines available which can be mounted on microscope stages can operate under ideal load conditions.

In attempting precision micro-indentation studies we are immediately confronted with the problem of surface preparation of the specimen. It is well known that mechanical polishing can work-harden a surface. The depth of penetration of micro-indents is small, often a few microns, at times even less than a micron. If a surface is *mechanically* polished it is quite certain that the hardness of the upper layers is not that of the main body of material. Thus small micro-indents on such a surface will give a ' surface layer ' hardness which differs, sometimes a good deal, from that of the bulk material. Either macro-indents must be made so deeply as to penetrate the surface layer, or, alternatively, if micro-indents are required (and they are essential if small crystallites or small regions, such as carburized hardened surface layers are under study) then a surface preparation is required which is free from distortion due to mechanical polish.

We have solved the surface problem for some specific studies in three quite separate ways using (*a*) casting, or (*b*) electrolytic polish, or (*c*) cleavage. The casting method is suited to low-melting-point metals like tin and bismuth. Electrolytic polish is excellent with many alloys. Cleavage can be used in limited cases, e.g. with zinc crystals, which after cooling in liquid air, can be cleaved to give surfaces of very beautiful interferometric quality.

Tin

The casting of single crystals of tin (or the securing of large single crystallites within a melt) is simple. Tin is melted and poured on to a glass plate warmed to about 240° C. When allowed to cool slowly, the tin conforms to the surface of the glass and produces a surface of excellent interferometric quality. It is very easily scratched when handled and often in fact when an interferometer plate is matched against it. X-ray examination shows the diffraction pattern of a good single crystal with discrete spots permitting identification of crystal planes. Crystals have random orientation, in general, relative to the surface.

A pyramid indentation on tin, of a suitable size, is produced by a load of only 100 g. An interferogram for such an indentation is shown in Plate 245 (× 30). The surface flow is remarkable and shows a striking orientation. Two particular features should be noted. First it was established that all indents made on any one crystal face show the same orientation, which is clearly crystallographic ; second it is found that the pile-up pattern is not determined by the orientation of the indenter. The square base of the indenter, when turned round, has only a secondary effect on the pattern.

Examination of the indent flow pattern with fringes of equal chromatic order prove that the assymetry is much more marked than it appears. For in fact the two extensive wings prove to be pile-up elevations, whilst at right angles to these the smaller patterns are depressions, and therefore represent sink-in regions. The actual outline of the depression has an interesting related effect. This is shown to better advantage on an indent made with a smaller load and Plate 246 (× 140) is a microphotograph of an indent on the crystal. Two opposite sides are convex, the sides showing the extensive pile-up wings, and two are concave, those showing the sink-in.

The pile-up region in Plate 245 is about six light waves high (some 3 microns) but the sink-in region is only half as deep. When compared with the indents on steels and other alloys, this single-crystal indent is found to show distortions which extend to a much further distance from the centre of the indent. Surface distortion is appreciable to a distance of at least *six* diagonals, in the largely affected direction. This has two important consequences, not formerly realized. First, if more than one indent is to be placed on such a crystal, they must be separated by at

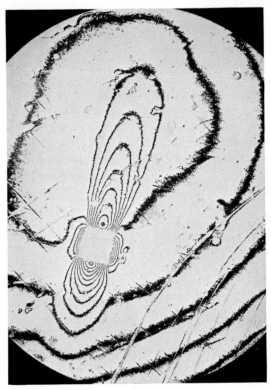

245

246

247

Plates 245-247

least *twelve* times the diagonal. This is very much more than the $\times 2\frac{1}{2}$ specified by British Standards Institute for homogeneous materials. A second, even more important, consequence concerns any attempt to evaluate the local hardness of individual crystallites, precipitates and crystal grains in multiple-phase alloys. For clearly, unless the boundaries of the grain are distant at least six times the diagonal, then edge and boundary effects will intervene. This means in general that the area of a crystallite to be measured must be a good deal bigger than investigators who work in this field have up to now realized. The field is an important one. For example in Sn-Sb bearings there are small local hard crystals within an extensive soft matrix and a knowledge of the hardness of the small crystals is desirable. It is in such instances where a recognition of the required crystal size is important.

The orientation of the distortion is clearly crystallographic. Furthermore closer scrutiny shows that the indent has produced slip lines. An X-ray analysis for the case shown in Plate 245 established that the direction of sink-in was along the projection of the c-axis on to the plane of the surface. In this instance the c-axis was accidentally lying almost in the surface itself. Although the height of pile-up in the directions perpendicular to the c-axis (the extensive wings) is similar on both sides, the distortion extends much further on one side than on the other. It was was established that this is due to the a- and b-axes making different angles with the surface.

It was clear from Plate 245 that the crystal has a marked differential directional effect and it is equally clear that the standard square-based diamond pyramid is not suited as an indenter to study this directional feature. We have therefore adopted the double-cone indenter designed by Grodzinski for the study of directional hardness effects on crystals.

Directional Studies with the Double Cone Indenter

Two types of indenter have been developed which are suitable for *directional* hardness studies, the elongated rhomb of Knoop and the double-cone of Grodzinski. The Knoop rhomb is a four-sided pyramid in which one diagonal is some seven times the other. It produces an indent with depth only 1/20th of the length. Experience shows that recovery effects are only noticeable as a reduction of the shorter diagonal whilst the length, which is not seriously affected, is taken as a measure of the hardness. The double-cone has all the advantages of the Knoop and is easier to construct. The geometry is that of two opposing cones on a common circular base, but on either side of this. It is, of course, polished from a single diamond. It produces a narrow, boat-shaped indent and again recovery only occurs in the width, so that the length becomes an effective measure of hardness. By placing the cone in different directions, directional effects can be studied. From the geometry of the indenter a double-cone hardness number can be computed as load divided by the area of the indent. Grodzinski has established a consistent correlation between the hardness values given by the Vickers pyramid and by the double cone.

As is now well established, deformation in single metal crystals is a result of two processes, slip and twinning. In slip the deformation resembles the parallel glide movement in a displaced pack of cards and can be recognized by visible slip lines. The stress required to produce slip depends on the orientation. There is a critical resolved shear-stress below which slip only occurs if these lower stresses are applied for a long time, and the effect is then termed ' creep '. In twinning, a displaced lamella is turned into a new orientation but still retains a common plane with the initial lattice plane, this being called the twin plane. It is to be expected that double-cone indentations on a crystal will penetrate more or less easily according to whether parallel or across slip directions and, indeed, that this is so will be demonstrated interferometrically.

The double-cone indenters in our possession were presented by Grodzinski. One section is circular, of radius 2 mm and perpendicular to this it is V-shaped with included angle 154°. Defining the hardness as load W divided by area, calculation shows that this can be converted into the form, Hardness $= W/cd^3$ in which d is the length of the indent and c is a constant. The width, and especially the depth, are only a small fraction of the length. In a typical indent on soft material the width is about 1/6th of the length and the depth is only 1/100th of the length. In the Vickers pyramid the depth is 1/7th of the length so that in fact the double cone is not only useful for measuring directional hardness, it is ideally suited for measuring the hardness of *thin layers*, such as electroplates. Plate 247 ($\times$ 100) shows a typical double-cone indent on tin. Careful inspection shows slip lines, parallel to the long axis.

An interferogram of such an indent with a 50 g load is shown in Plate 248 ($\times$ 80). There are two pile-up lobes symmetrically placed and within these, small slip-steps of height less than 200 Å can be detected.

The pattern is remarkably different when the diameter is placed nearly at right angles. This is shown in Plate 249 ($\times$ 80). In this we have an extensive pile-up, *in one direction only*. The disturbance extends for *twelve times* the width of the indent, which is again in conformity with our recognition that the British Standards Institute

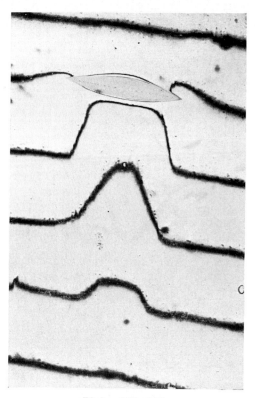

248

249

Plates 248, 249

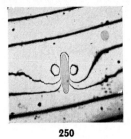
250

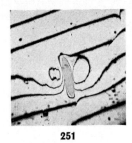
251

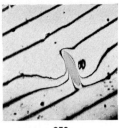
252

253

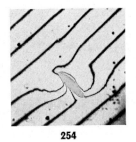
254

255

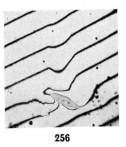
256

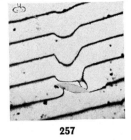
257

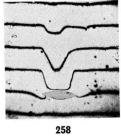
258

Plates 250-258

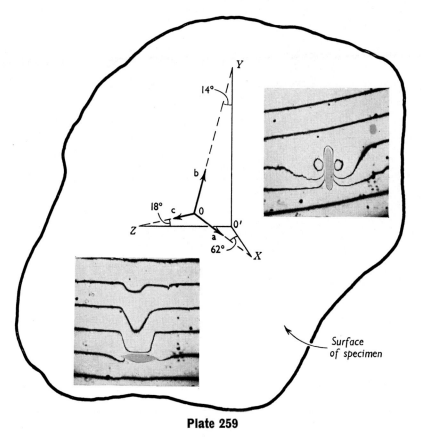

Plate 259

specification for separation of indents must be drastically altered when dealing with single crystals.

The length of the indent on Plate 248 is 35 mm and on Plate 249 it is 32 mm. The computed hardness in the first case is 1·4 and in the second 2·1. Clearly there is a differential effect with indents respectively parallel or perpendicular to the slip traces.

A succession of indents at 10° orientation interval has been made and a comparison between these is shown in Plates 250 to 258 (× 25). The slip directions are particularly clearly seen in Plates 251 and 255. Measurements like these enable a polar plot of the hardness variation to be made.

The results obtained depend entirely upon the real crystal axes

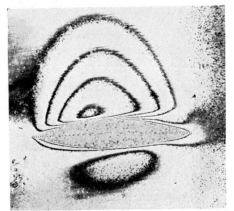

260

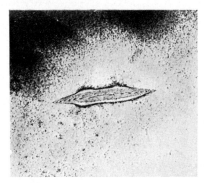

261

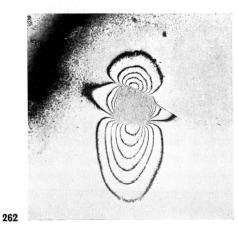

262

Plates 260-262

directions and these can only be determined by X-rays. For the case under consideration the orientations are shown in Plate 259.

Here OX, OY, OZ are the crystal axes and O′X, O′Y, O′Z their projections on the crystal plane being indented. The minimum hardness is that when the long axis of the indenter is parallel to O′Y and the maximum hardness when it is perpendicular to this.

There is one further feature to which attention has not yet been drawn. In interferograms like Plate 248, for example, the number of fringes *within* the indent can be clearly counted (in this case 25), thus the depth of the indent can be computed also.

It is only intended in this treatise to illustrate the possibilities of the interferometric approach and there is no intention of analysing the considerable quantity of data available, yet even the example shown clearly relates the flow pattern to crystallographic direction and proves that the hardness is determined by the degree of interference with slip lines. As a further example an illustration taken from bismuth is instructive.

The casting of bismuth on glass did not produce so good a surface finish as that given by tin, nevertheless the interferograms were good enough to show the slip directions. Plate 260 ($\times$ 100) for a 50 g load shows an indent with the long axis parallel to slip lines and Plate 261 ($\times$ 100) an indent with the same load, but set perpendicular to them. The slip lines break up the fringes in Plate 260. A polar plot for bismuth shows that the hardness ranges in value from 1·5 in the parallel position to no less than 6·8. A 50 g Vickers Pyramid indention shown in Plate 262 ($\times$ 90) for bismuth is closely related to that of tin, with two extended pile-up directions, and two sink-in regions at right angles. This picture is of interest in that a twinning is revealed in the lower sink-in region.

Finally, the findings up to date by interferometry in this field may be summarized as follows. The fringes show that the direction of piling up is a crystal property and not affected by the orientation of the indenter. The observed pile-up differs on the two sides of the indentation, and as the indenter is rotated the pile-up goes through maxima and minima. The fringes prove that slip-traces are associated with the pile-up and one can infer from fringe curvature that considerable microslip takes place too which is not resolved by the microscope but which integrates to curve the fringe. Hardness is a minimum in the direction parallel to the slip traces and in this position the deformation is then a maximum. Interferometry demonstrates too, that the observed variations in indentation length are accompanied by parallel variations in width and in depth, but these are accentuated by recovery. For instance in Plates 248 and 249 the length ratios are 1·09 but the depth ratios 1·19, a small but quite definite difference, due to recovery.

REFERENCES

Nos. 25, 28, 35, 45, J, N, S.

19. INDUCTION OF PERCUSSION RING CRACKS ON DIAMOND

The diamond ball indenter—Octahedral faces—Dodecahedral faces—A cubic face—Percussion with a tungsten carbide ball—References.

The Diamond Ball Indenter

DURING a careful interferometric study of a large number of diamond octahedral faces, it was frequently noticed that there existed on such faces small crystallographically oriented, hexagonal-shaped markings. These are usually small, less than 1/50th mm across and are only readily recognized in smooth, good quality regions. They occur with surprising frequency and their boundaries can be developed up into sharp vivid contrast by etching methods. Indeed, it was during our numerous etching experiments that we first became conscious of the relative ubiquity of these markings. They are strictly oriented, with sides parallel to the edges of the octahedral faces. It was conjectured that these were percussion marks, for it was argued that despite the great hardness of diamond, its easy cleavage in the three favourable directions could well lead to the formation of a hexagonally-shaped percussion mark if the diamond were subject to impact by a fairly hard body. A series of experiments was thereupon undertaken, the object of which was an attempt to induce ring cracks artificially. We quickly established that such oriented percussion marks are quite easy to induce and an interferometric study of these has produced much of interest, and also some features quite difficult to understand in connection with the behaviour of diamond under load.

Octahedral Faces. The first artificially induced rings were made on octahedral faces, actually on the large plane faces of flat portrait stones. A considerable advantage attaches to the use of such a stone in that it permits of simultaneous interferometric observation *through* the stone (from below) with two-beam interferometry, whilst load is being applied from above. Since diamond is so much harder than other materials, it was decided in the first instance to apply pressure to the flat portrait stone with a *ball-ended diamond*. This impacter was specially made for the purpose. It was a diamond cylinder with a hemispherical ball-end of diameter 0·78 mm.   It was specially prepared on a machine designed for the purpose by P. Grodzinski.   An octahedron diamond was first ground into cylindical shape and the tip then polished to a hemisphere, such that the tangent plane at the end, normal to the cylinder axis, was the cubic plane of the diamond.   This was then mounted into the indenter holder of a commercial hardness indenting machine (Penetrascope) and, with this, known loads up to 30 kg could be applied.   Before making impacts the radius of curvature and perfection of finish of the diamond hemisphere were assessed interferometrically, and we were satisfied that the geometry was a close approach to hemispherical.

Load was applied between the ball and the plane and the sequence of events was followed visually (and photographically).   The sequence is shown in Plates 263, 264, 265 (all × 80).   The first picture, Plate 263, shows the appearance when the load is 0·5 kg.   The true area of contact is shown by the black spot, which is the familiar black spot at the centre of Newton's rings and arises through the differential phase change on reflection at air-diamond and diamond-air.   This is valuable, since it permits us to compute the exact load per unit area which the plane diamond is supporting.   Plate 264 shows the increased area of contact when the load is raised to 2·5 kg.   Suddenly at 5 kg (Plate 265) a hexagonal ring crack appears round the perimeter of the circle of contact and in fact the sharp sound of a crack is heard at this moment.

As long as the load is maintained the hexagonal crack exhibits three dark lobes coming out from three alternate sides.   These are internal defects which we have indeed studied, but here our immediate purpose is to show how the application of surface topographical interferometric techniques have contributed to the problem, and no attempt will be made to go into the somewhat lengthy analysis we have made elsewhere of the crack phenomena *within* the body of the crystal.

The character of the oriented crack produced by this surprisingly small load is shown at higher magnification in Plate 266 (× 350), which is the permanent pattern left on the flat diamond after removal of the load.   It is small and very shallow, as will be established shortly, and only appears here vividly because it has been photographed with a sensitive phase-contrast microscope.   It will be noticed that the hexagonal outline is surrounded by a light border, which is the effect produced in phase-contrast by a slight elevation.   The true interpretation of this is given by multiple-beam interferometry, as will be shown shortly.

Since the Newton's ring black spot gives the exact area of contact, this is readily obtained at the critical cracking stage so that the true

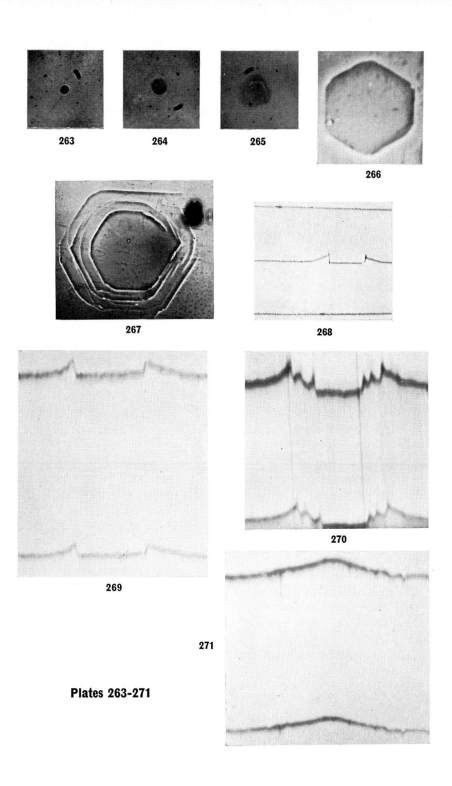

263

264

265

266

267

268

269

270

271

Plates 263-271

breaking stress can be derived. Although the applied load was small (a few kg) the area of contact when failure took place was only some 0·0035 sq mm. From this the stress to induce a crack is some $1·2 \times 10^{11}$ dyn/cm^2, which is higher than one would at first imagine when so small a load is applied. On different stones, and at different regions of the same stone, cracks commence at loads which vary between 3·5 and 5 kg, due no doubt to true local variations in strength.

When a heavier load is applied, then a multiple crack forms, an example for a 12-kg load being shown in Plate 267 ($\times$ 400). We shall call the first, single, crack the ' primary ' crack and the succeeding pattern a ' compound ' crack.

A multiple-beam interferogram which shows the surface topographical changes accompanying a primary crack is shown in Plate 268 ($\times$ 100). An alternative approach is to use fringes of equal chromatic order and such fringes across a primary crack are shown in Plate 269 ($\times$ 300) at a higher magnification. Corresponding fringes across a compound crack are shown in Plate 270 ($\times$ 300). These fringes exhibit some remarkable characteristics. They reveal on the surface of the diamond *evidence of a smooth pile-up outside of the crack*. Such a pile-up for a primary crack is found to be always less than a mere 300 Å in height. Approaching from outside the surface rises smoothly then drops abruptly at the crack. The drop is not quite perpendicular but the fall of 300 Å takes place over a distance of the order of 1/200 mm, which means that the angle deviates but very slightly from the vertical, yet it is measurable. Within the hexagonal outline of the crack, the base is here as near as can be measured at the same level as the outer undisturbed region.

In a compound crack this smooth rise and sudden drop repeats itself at each crack ledge boundary. By far the most remarkable feature is the unexpected appearance of the smooth pile-up. Its presence can be demonstrated in another way. Plate 271 ($\times$ 300) shows fringes of equal chromatic order taken *outside*, but close to, the edge of a primary crack. The minor irregularities in this, which are on quite a small scale, are due to surface structure features inherent to the crystal before beginning the experiment, for it was not, of course, a perfect plane. Considering the high magnification and high dispersion, the fringe definition is good, and adequately establishes the existence of a smooth pile-up in the region outside of the ring crack.

One might not have expected a smooth displacement ; rather, on the contrary, slip trace discontinuities might have been anticipated. Neither the highest precision fringes, nor a sensitive phase-contrast microscope reveal the slightest evidence of any slip lines. It must be concluded that on this scale the diamond is smoothly and continuously deformed. One can envisage two possible but conflicting explanations, either of which is difficult to understand. First, it could be conjectured that there has been a *plastic flow* similar to that which leads to pile-up in the case of an indented metal. Since these experiments were made at room temperature any such plastic flow for diamond is totally unexpected. Alternatively it could be conjectured that when the crack forms, minute crystal debris fills in the underlying gaps. We have indeed established from studies on the dark lobes already mentioned that there are internal cracks lying in the cleavage directions, but then these close up when the load is removed. Even so, let us postulate that some debris does permanently occupy these lobes, in which case the surface displacement might then be attributable to a permanent *elastic deformation*.

This conjecture of a *permanent* elastic deformation also appears to be very improbable. There are good crystallographic reasons accounting for why only three dark lobes are seen and not six. Furthermore it is usual to find an asymmetry in the fringe pattern. If dispersion is arranged such that a fringe bisects two opposite sides, a greater pile-up is observed on the side associated with the lobe. Linked to this is the occasional appearance of hexagons in which three alternate sides are longer than the others, the longer sides showing the lobes.

A further surface feature appears which gives supporting evidence for the existence of a micro-plastic flow. This is the fact that at times with primary cracks, and always with compound cracks, the central flat hexagon region can be depressed, perhaps 100 Å below the undisturbed outer region. In both primary and compound cracks the volume of the pile-up is perhaps largely accounted for by the space created in the appearance of the cleavage cracks. The existence of an actual volume compression is most improbable. We are inclined to believe that the diamond does actually suffer a micro-plastic flow, but if the effect is really due to a succession of micro-slips then their effects are well below our limit of resolution interferometrically.

The stress figure of $1 \cdot 2 \times 10^{11}$ dyn/cm^2 is considerably less than one might have expected in view of the very great hardness of diamond, but the explanation is simple. The reason is that the hexagon is essentially a pattern which develops along *easy cleavage directions*. It is clear that this onset of a percussion ring crack probably plays an important part in the fracture and ultimate failure of high-speed machine cutting diamond tools and drill crowns. It is to be anticipated that

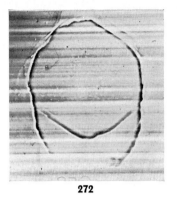

272

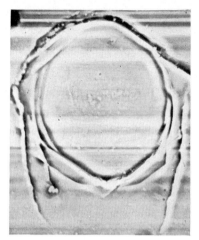

273

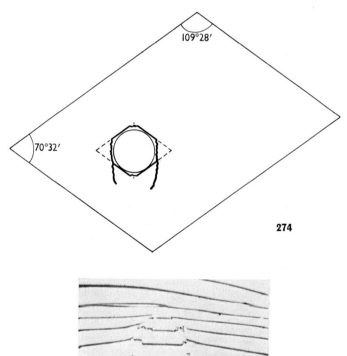

109°28′

70°32′

274

275

Plates 272-275

machining processes involving local great stresses will lead to the formation of a ring crack, and from such an origin more widespread fracture
will initiate and develop.

Percussion on the Dodecahedral Plane. Almost invariably dodecahedral faces are rounded, often striated, and at times covered with an
elaborate network pattern. All these factors together prevent the study
in general of these minute percussion marks on natural dodecahedral
faces. We therefore sectioned and roughly polished a diamond along
the dodecahedral plane, or at least on a plane closely approximating to
the true dodecahedral plane direction. Pressure marks were successfully produced on this face which was smooth enough for an interferometric study.

The primary cracks required a higher load than that needed for the
octahedral face, no primary crack on the dodecahedral plane being
obtained with a load of less than 7 kg with the same spherical diamond
impactor as used before. Such a load produces again a primary crack
but most of such primaries exhibit two ' tails '. Plate 272 (× 360) is
characteristic, being obtained with 7 kg. Increase in load, as on the
octahedral faces, also leads to a compound crack, an example obtained
with 24 kg being shown in Plate 273 (× 360). The orientation of the
sides of the crack relative to the sides of the dodecahedral rhomb face is
shown in Plate 274.

The interferograms for the dodecahedral face ring crack show a close
resemblance to those secured from the octahedral faces. Plate 275
(× 140) is typical. In the pattern in Plate 272, the straight sides lie in
the principal cleavage directions of the diamond. Here we have new
evidence of the reputed secondary dodecahedral cleavage also. There
has been some uncertainty as to whether or not there is a secondary
dodecahedral cleavage direction in addition to the familiar octahedral
cleavage direction. The two sides with the tails are evidence of a true,
but imperfect, cleavage in directions other than the octahedral. This
secondary cleavage is clearly imperfect, as shown by the irregularity
and the wriggled tail. The primary crack on the dodecahedral face
requires a stress of some 1.8×10^{11} dyn/cm^2, which is some 50%
greater than that for octahedral faces (roughly 50%, in so far as there is
variation from place to place, and stone to stone, and these constitute
average figures).

Percussion on the Cubic Face. We had available a natural diamond
cube (an uncommon form) which was, as most often, opaque and full
of minute inclusions. A crude polish was secured on a cubic face and
this was subject to indent from the diamond ball. Square-shaped

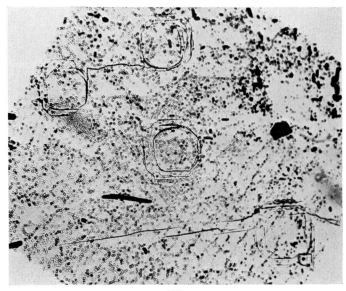

276

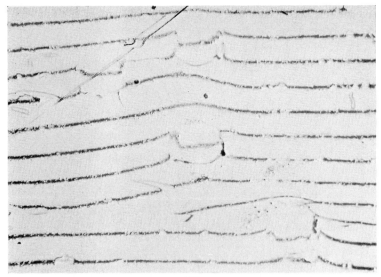

277

Plates 276-277

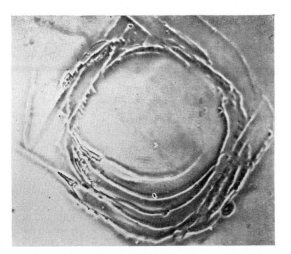

278

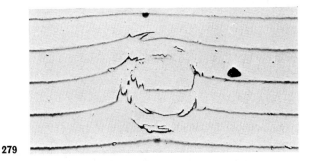

279

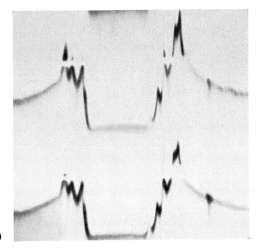

280

Plates 278-280

percussion marks were produced, but these needed a still higher stress, namely $2 \cdot 0 \times 10^{11}$ dyn/cm^2. No crack could be induced with a load of less than 20 kg, by which load the diamond ball itself was appreciably elastically deformed. This explains why so big a load has not produced a corresponding increase in stress. Plate 276 ($\times$ 120) shows some of the square-shaped cracks induced on this face. The surface is rough and dotted with numerous inclusions, yet the outlines of the cracks can be seen clearly. The best interferogram obtainable is that shown in Plate 277 ($\times$ 120) and despite its crudity it is a valuable picture. For it shows without any doubt at all that the surface distortion connected with the crack extends over a very considerable area. Furthermore the actual height of the associated pile-up is a good deal more than in the corresponding cracks on the other faces. It is here nearly 1200 Å.

The poor character of this natural face induced us to truncate and polish an octahedron to give an approximate cubic plane which was reasonably flat. This was then submitted to indentation. One single crack only was secured, at a load of 29 kg, and this is shown in Plate 278 ($\times$ 400). It is a complex square-shaped crack. By focussing beneath the surface it was established that within the body of the crystal there is violent extensive crack disturbance associated with this indentation. It is emphasized that although the surface was kept under constant observation no primary crack formed and this compound pattern was the first indication of any cracking having taken place, the stress needed being $2 \cdot 0 \times 10^{11}$ dyn/cm^2. An interferogram across this crack is shown in Plate 279 ($\times$ 180). Fringes of equal chromatic order sectioning this crack are shown in Plate 280 ($\times$ 210).

It was found that the diamond ball indenter itself had failed and cracked violently when this percussion mark was made and this brought these particular experiments to an end. Owing to the untimely decease of P. Grodzinski no other diamond ball became available to us.

Both the natural and the polished cubic faces give evidence of the existence of a considerable plastic-type flow pile-up. This can be inferred from several lines of argument. For these percussion marks the depression of the flat inner portion encompassed by the crack lines is very marked indeed. This can attain a value of as much as some 500 Å, as evidenced by the fringes of equal chromatic order shown in Plate 281 ($\times$ 200). The surrounding raised pile-up reaches the relatively considerable value of 2000 Å, far bigger than on the other faces. A particularly revealing interferogram is that on Plate 282 ($\times$ 200) which shows at high magnification and high dispersion the fringes of equal

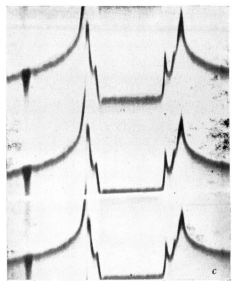

281

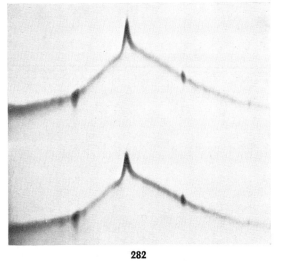

282

Plates 281, 282

chromatic order given by a region close to but *outside* of the square figure. The smooth pile-up to no less than 2000 Å is clearly shown. The section chosen for this picture was parallel to the diagonal of the square percussion mark and it reveals how the surface pile-up rises to a sharp peak as the corner is passed and then falls off. This is quite the contrary to what happens when a pyramid indent is made in a metal surface.

In the experiments made with the rough, natural, cube the central depression exceeds the volume piled up. It is most likely that the explanation lies in the considerable impurity content, obvious from the inclusions. It is more than likely that such a crystal could suffer appreciable compression under the load.

Thus we see that the octahedron face is the least resistant, the cubic face the most resistant, and the dodecahedron face lies in between. The resistance of the cubic face to cracking is such that when it does ultimately crack it releases considerable energy and this is responsible for the severe internal damage associated with the cubic face ring crack.

As already mentioned the experiments using a diamond ball impactor were brought to an end by the failure of this impactor when in contact with a cubic face. The tangent plane of the diamond ball was itself a cubic face and as such it was wisely chosen, since events demonstrated that such a face was the most resistant. On the diamond ball tip was found the trace of a roughly square ring crack. It was the initial choice of a cubic tangent plane which enabled the ball impactor to survive impact against the relatively softer octahedron and dodecahedron planes. Clearly when cube contacts cube, both give way by ring crack formation, ultimately. Of particular interest was a redetermination of the radius of curvature of the central tip of the ball. This was within the square crack mark and had of course taken the main burden of stress in all the indents made (some dozens, including eight on the rough natural cube and that leading to the final collapse on the one polished cube). The radius of the undisturbed portion was evaluated interferometrically and found to have increased from the initial value of 0·39 mm to a new value of 0·50 mm. Here again is further evidence of a *permanent* micro deformation in the character of a micro-plastic flow, in conformity with all the other observations concerning this aspect of the behaviour of the diamond.

Percussion with a Tungsten Carbide Ball

Whilst all these experiments, especially the valuable interferograms, throw light on the behaviour of diamond versus diamond, they do not account for the very frequent occurrence of minute percussion marks on natural diamonds. For the chance collision of diamond against diamond in the natural Kimberlite ore must be very remote, judging from the known relative paucity of distribution of diamond in the ore. It was therefore conjectured that the percussion marks on the mined diamonds might be a product of the crushing mechanism used in grinding down the ore for separation. For the mining procedures are now highly mechanized and the ore is crushed by machinery first, the diamonds then being extracted by washing over grease tables. It became therefore necessary to establish whether in fact a material *softer* than diamond could induce percussion ring cracks on the diamond itself. Our experiments have shown that ring cracks on diamond can be produced both by sapphire balls and by tungsten carbide balls, both of which have a Vickers' Hardness Number of the order of 1750, which is considerably less than that of diamond itself (a numerical value for diamond is most uncertain, but there is no doubt that the hardness is well away above 2000. Reported data are very variable and extend from 6000 to some 50,000. A value of at least 10,000 appears to be a reasonable conservative estimate). The experiments we have made with the tungsten carbide balls have proved most profitable and deserve to be discussed here. The balls used were a commercial product. They were not particularly smooth, but were reasonably good spheres of diameter 1 mm. With these, pressure was applied successively to octahedral, dodecahedral and cubic faces in turn. Since a plentiful supply was available new balls were frequently used.

With the 1-mm tungsten ball applied to an octahedron face of diamond a primary crack initiated at 16 kg, and this ultimately became compound when the load reached 30 kg. *No cracks could be initiated at all with our maximum load of 30 kg on either the dodecahedral or the cubic faces* by impacting with these carbide balls. It is here re-emphasized that, so far, we have never yet seen ring cracks on the best *dodecahedral* surfaces we have studied, although we have available a reasonable number of very fine dodecahedra. On the other hand they are repeatedly found on natural *octahedral* faces. The experiment seems to suggest that on the more sensitive octahedral face even softer material, like quartz, might succeed in producing the effects found. It must be stressed that so far our experiments are relatively *static*, i.e. load is applied slowly. The sharp blow in crushing machinery may make a tremendous difference since it is well known that cleavage mechanisms are always most easily initiated by sharp blows. We do intend later taking up the study of *dynamic* impact and would not be in the least surprised to find

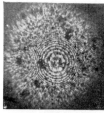

283

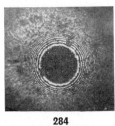

284

285

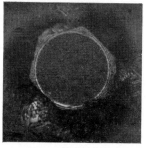

286

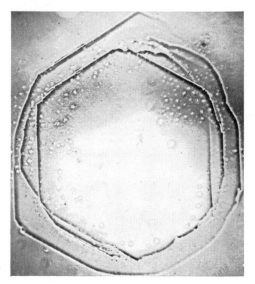

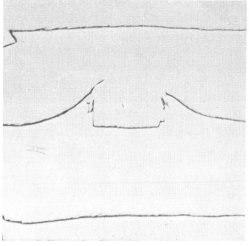

287

288

Plates 283-288

the effects considerably enhanced by such an impact. It is re-emphasized that the ring crack initiates through cleavage, that cleavage is induced easily by a blow and that the carbide in a static experiment induces the cracks easily, from which it might well be conjectured that a softer material in a dynamic experiment might prove equally efficacious.

The carbide ball requires a higher load than a diamond ball of the same radius because its tip flattens under the load when it is pressed against the diamond. We have been able to trace the complete evolution of an octahedral ring crack produced by a carbide ball in a striking fashion. Selecting from the numerous pictures obtained, the appearance at successive loads of 0, 3, 9, 16 kg are shown in Plates 283, 284, 285 and 286 (all at $\times$ 160). A perfect regular crack initiates at 16 kg. On increasing the load to 30 kg the final pattern obtained is that shown in Plate 287 ($\times$ 350). An interferogram at about half magnification of this is shown in Plate 288 ($\times$ 150) which illustrates the fringes bisecting opposite sides. Plate 289 ($\times$ 220) illustrates the fringes of equal chromatic order for the fringes in a section bisecting opposite angles.

Once again the familiar regular smooth rise to a pile-up is very clearly shown. There is particularly good definition in Plate 289 and as the lateral magnification is $\times$ 220 one can assert with some confidence that there is no visible trace of a discontinuous slip line effect. Notable are : (1) the symmetry of the system ; (2) the pile-up height which reaches to 1000 Å ; and (3) the clearly evident central depression which measurement shows is some 300 Å below the initial original level. Attention is once more drawn to the very great magnification in depth which is achieved on such an interferogram. It is here nearly 200,000 times, but as horizontal magnification is 220 times, the vertical scale is actually almost *1000 times* the horizontal scale. Thus it will be recognized that all the arguments being pressed here in favour of a plastic flow refer to effects on a very micro scale indeed.

The tungsten balls were always deformed by the impact, and suffered permanent flattening. The two-beam Newton's rings patterns for a ball before and after use are shown respectively in Plates 290 ($\times$ 300) and 291 ($\times$ 300). Before the tests the ball was an excellent sphere with radius of curvature 0·54 mm. After use for producing ring cracks, the central region, over a range of 0·13 mm diameter had a radius of curvature some three times as big as before, i.e. it had flattened to a radius of 1·56 mm. It is of interest to note that the stress computed for the primary ring crack produced with the 16 kg on the carbide ball was to all intents and purposes identical with that computed for the diamond ball. Even at 30 kg the stress was little higher, owing to the ball

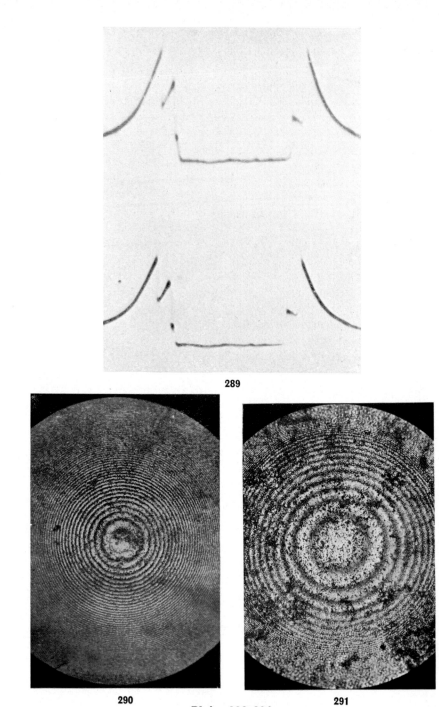

289

290

291

Plates 289-291

flattening. This explains why, with the carbide ball at 30 kg, one secures a larger ring crack but still a well-defined one.

These experiments, having established that it is not necessary to impact diamond on diamond to induce a ring crack, indicate that a further field of profitable study might result from the successive use of materials softer than the carbide.

REFERENCES

Nos. 44, 47, 52, P.

PART SEVEN

STUDIES OF IMPACTS ON METALS
DIAMOND ABRASION RESISTANCE
WEAR OF GLAZIER'S DIAMONDS

20. SOME SURFACE DISTORTION EFFECTS

Ultra-sonic drilling of glass and metals—Spark erosion pits on metals—High-speed impact distortions—Impacts on Perspex, on Duraluminium, on suspended water drops—References.

Surface Distortions Associated with Ultra-sonic Drilling

WITHIN recent years two machining processes have been developed on an extensive industrial scale for specialized purposes. These use respectively ultra-sonic impact and electric-spark erosion and both techniques are now fully established commercial procedures either for drilling and cutting unusual shapes or for processing very hard alloys. We have begun some preliminary studies on the surface-flow phenomena which accompany these machining processes and, although these researches are in a very early stage, we can report some progress already. This section will be devoted to some studies made with a small ultra-sonic drill and in the succeeding section the electric erosion process will be reported upon.

The ultra-sonic machine used was the small Mullard 50-watt ultra-sonic drill, vibrating at 20 kc/s. The cutting tool, which can have a complex shape if wished, rests on the work-piece in a slurry of silicon carbide abrasive mixed with water. Since the cutting tool itself can be formed of a soft metal, such as brass, unusual shapes, such as squares, hexagons, etc., can be cut directly into very hard metal, a matter of much value in the machining of hard alloys. It is known that the cutting rate depends on frequency, amplitude, hardness of abrasive used, tool shape, concentration of slurry and on the efficient flow of slurry.

In cutting holes in glass discs, we have established by interferometry that a distinct difference in surface-flow pattern appears according to whether a continuous flow or a hand feed is used in supplying the slurry to the workpiece. Thus, for example, Plate 292 (× 15) shows an interferogram over a sheet of glass into which has been ultra-sonically drilled a hole of diameter 3·3 mm, using manual feed of the slurry. The fringes reveal an appreciable ' sink-in ' surrounding the drilled hole. This may possibly be due to a local melting of the glass. Plate 293 (× 15) shows on the contrary the interference pattern surrounding a similar drilled hole in which all conditions were the same with the exception that the

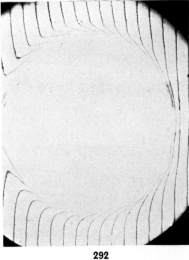

292

293

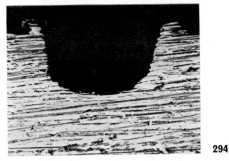

294

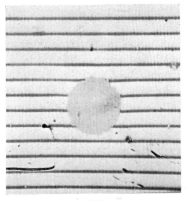
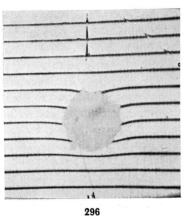

295

296

Plates 292-296

slurry was continuously fed and changed. This time there is no trace at all of a ' sink-in ', for the fringes run straight up to the edge of the drilled hole. The difference is not, of course, very marked and it may well be that the whole effect is due to a difference in the efficiency of cooling and to nothing else.

When a metal plate is drilled with the ultra-sonic machine there is usually a considerable ' pile-up ', so large, in fact, that its presence is quite easily demonstrated by simple sectioning. An example is shown in Plate 294 ($\times$ 50). This is naturally a destructive test and as it is often desirable to evaluate surface flow features by non-destructive methods, interferometry is admirably suited, provided the pile-up is much less violent than that shown in Plate 294, for on this plate the effect is too big for interferometry. However, in many cases the flow is on a much smaller scale and such small-scale effects can be suitably studied by interferometry.

We have established that the extent of the pile-up distortion which surrounds a drilled hole depends upon the size of the abrasive particles constituting the slurry. Plate 295 ($\times$ 25) shows an interferogram for a hole drilled in a glass plate using 600-mesh Carborundum powder. There is no visible pile-up. However, Plate 296 ($\times$ 25) shows the interferogram obtained when the hole was drilled under similar conditions, but using instead a coarser 240-mesh Carborundum abrasive. The surrounding surface now exhibits a clearly marked deformation, although slight. The displacement nowhere exceeds 900 Å.

As was only to be expected the surface pile-up produced depends upon the hardness of the workpiece, the softer the material the greater the pile-up. This effect is demonstrated in Plates 297, 298, 299 and 300 (all at $\times$ 25). These constitute a set of interferograms surrounding slots cut into metals of progressively increasing hardness. Displacement to the right means a pile-up. Plate 297 refers to a sheet of nickel of hardness number 80 and there is considerable distortion near the edges. Plate 298 is for brass, which had a hardness 120 and again there is distortion near the edge, but much less than in the case of the nickel. Plate 299 shows the effect observed for a mild steel plate of hardness 420. The pile-up is appreciably less than in the case of brass. Finally, Plate 300 shows the interferogram for a hard tool-steel of hardness 800. Pile-up is slight and highly localized near the edge.

It is well known that the ultra-sonic drilling mechanism is a complex involving many separate variables. It is hoped to continue these studies further. In the following section some studies made on the erosion of metal surfaces by electric sparks will be considered.

297

298

299

300

Plates 297-300

Spark Erosion Pits

The study of the pits produced by single sparks is of interest in two technological fields. The first is the obvious one of the wear of electric make-break contacts which are so extensively employed. As a rule the currents are small, but they may be large. The second field, that in which we are interested here, is that of electric spark erosion, in which metal machining is conducted through erosion by a rapid succession of heavy-current single or multiple sparks. A shaped electrode is used and this eats its way into the workpiece producing a hole of desired shape. The studies described here refer only to the sparks produced by single high-current pulses.

The following electrical arrangements were found suitable. Plane parallel polished or ground electrodes were separated by about 1 mm, either in gas or in an oil. Studies have been made both with high-melting-point and low-melting-point metals. Since the aim was the study of single sparks it was necessary to quench the discharge and oil quenching was found suitable, for in a gas it was difficult to secure a single spark, the secondary ionization effects promoting multiple discharges. We have, however, made observations in air, argon and nitrogen as well as in oil. Circuitry was arranged in a pulse-forming network to give single constant-current short discharges and both the current and the time duration could be measured. Interferometric studies on the shapes of the pits formed by single sparks have given encouraging results and some typical observations will be recorded here. One object of the investigations was an attempt to measure the volume of metal eroded by a single discharge and this we have succeeded in doing for a variety of conditions. A second aim has been to study the geometric shapes of the pits, and for this interferometry is well suited.

Much has been written as to the sparking mechanism and on the mechanism of erosion, but little is known about the *shapes* of individual pits and this is where these studies can contribute. Although here only some multiple-beam interferograms are shown, we did in our researches use auxiliary optical methods for identifying the rather coarse features, i.e. for establishing up-down directions and so on. The spark pits we have studied were produced by condenser-inductance networks giving single sparks, of duration either 10 microseconds or 100 microseconds and a voltage up to 5000 volts was available. Electrodes studied were tungsten, steel, nickel, aluminium, zinc, cadmium, tin, lead and bismuth, thus encompassing a considerable melting-point range. Both finely ground and well-polished electrodes were used in turn and differences

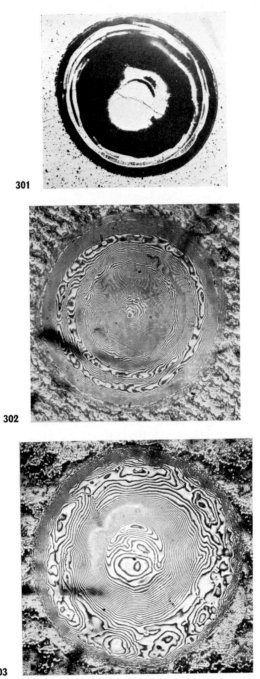

301

302

303

Plates 301-303

were found due to this. The current flowing through the single spark was registered with an oscilloscope display, and, during the 10 or the 100 microseconds, the discharge currents passing were recorded and were in the range 400 to 150 amperes, the higher currents being those of the shorter duration.

Some profitable interferometric data resulted from the study of the tungsten electrodes. First, it was established that the anode pit is always smoother and more amenable to interferometric examination than the corresponding cathode pit. Some of these will now be considered. Plate 301 ($\times$ 70) shows a photograph of an anode pit on tungsten given by a current of 175 amps passing for 100 microseconds. At first sight this does not appear to be too complicated, but the interferogram for this in Plate 302 ($\times$ 100) shows that the pit is a good deal more complex than the simple photograph reveals. If on the same electrodes the current is changed to 300 amps, lasting for 10 microseconds, the modified fringe pattern of Plate 303 ($\times$ 120) appears. With the aid of auxiliary optical systems it was established that these pictures are to be interpreted in the following way. Consider for example Plate 303. On approaching the pit from the outside there is first a steep irregular *rise*, a pile-up, in height about 5 light waves. Then follows a reasonably broad, flat, annular plateau, the region where fringe dispersion is large. This ring-form plateau is then followed by a regular conical drop *downwards* of depth some 12 waves, i.e. to a depth of some 7 waves below the original undisturbed surface. This conical pit runs down to a central fairly flat basal region. The pit is effectively a hole in the shape of a truncated cone, with material piled up craterwise above the original level. The bright ring and the bright central disc in Plate 301 are now seen to be the top of the flat annulus and the flat basal centre.

Reasonable estimates can be made for the various volumes involved, both for the pile-ups and the depressions. We have computed these for a succession of currents, with discharges lasting the same time. For example, with 10 microsecond discharges of 200, 300 and 400 amps, the pile-ups measured interferometrically are about 11, 11, 37 $\times$ 10^{-8} cm^3. Increasing the duration of the current to 100 microseconds has a marked effect. The pile-up for a 250-amp pit with 100 microsecond duration is about ten times as much as that for the same current with 10-microsecond duration. The pile-up is roughly proportional to the duration and the internal eroded volume follows in a similar way. To a rough approximation the volume eroded from the trough is not very different to that in the pile-up, but a really accurate comparison so as to establish

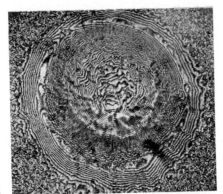

304

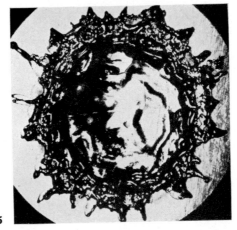

305

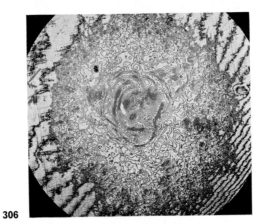

306

Plates 304-306

how much is vaporized is not possible. It is clear that the amount vaporized is quite a small fraction of the size of the hole ; most of the material is merely redistributed on the surface.

Ground surfaces are subject to an anomaly in that at times within the central hollow conical depression the surface can rise even above the initial main outer level. Our data on this are as yet confused and inconclusive, the main reason being that ground surfaces are difficult in that the sparks to them are often multiple instead of being single as on the polished surfaces. A typical *cathode* pit is shown in Plate 304 (× 150) for a 100-microsecond 250-amp discharge. Such pits are always more complex than the *anode* pits. Almost invariably those produced for the longer times and with the bigger currents exhibit elevations at the centre surrounded with an annular moat-like depression.

Pits with electrodes of soft metals defy interferometric analysis, for local melting leads to impossibly complex interference patterns. This is only too self-evident from Plate 305 (× 30) which shows a low magnification picture of a single pit on zinc. Molten globules and high irregularity make interferometric analysis very difficult. The almost impossible difficulty of securing any useful numerical data from a low-melting-point surface is well shown by Plate 306 (× 27) which reveals interferometrically the highly complex character of a single pit from one discharge on a surface of tin. Little can be deduced from such a picture, although it can be seen that there is multi-wrinkling into many local highly curved drops.

It can be concluded that the interferometric approach can yield information about the erosion pits produced on the surfaces of the higher-melting-point metals but has little to offer in connection with low-melting-point metals.

Pits Produced by High-speed Impact

A problem that has arisen in connection with high-speed air travel is that called ' rain-erosion '. It has been found that the fabric of an aircraft, both metal and plastic, especially when moving at supersonic speeds, can suffer serious damage if the aircraft flies through rain. The damage has a complex origin, including elastic and plastic effects and also wave-propagation complications. Both metal surfaces, like wings, and plastic surfaces, like Perspex windows, can suffer a surprising amount of damage. It was clear that the ultimate failures and fractures on the surface are determined by initial micro-cracks formed at an early stage and it was evident that such early stages would be amenable to an interferometric study. It was decided therefore to make a study of single

impact phenomena, i.e. the effects produced on plastic and metal surfaces by high-speed impact with a *single drop* or a *single sphere* in the
hope that some contribution might be made to the practical rain-erosion
problem.

Two approaches were developed. In the one case the rain-erosion
problem confronting the aircraft engineer was simulated by designing
an air gun and firing from it small cylinders of metal or Perspex at speeds
up to 1450 ft per second (1370 km an hour). These cylinders were fired
at suspended *single* water droplets and after recovery the damage produced by the impact studied by means of interferometry. In the second
approach, metal spheres and also polythene spheres, were fired directly
at sheets of metal or of Perspex. In both cases the velocities of the
projectiles were determined with electronic equipment. By these experiments comparison could be made by impact with : (*a*) a liquid sphere ;
(*b*) a soft, deformable plastic sphere ; and (*c*) a hard metal sphere. A
basic aim was an attempt to secure some relationship between the
velocity of impact and the volume of material affected by the impact,
which in fact we succeeded in doing over the velocity range studied.
This success is entirely attributable to the employment of interferometry to assess the damage.

The illustrations of the damage created shall be largely multiple-
beam Fizeau fringe patterns, but fringes of equal chromatic order have
also been extensively employed for the investigation. Although a rain-
storm leads to a *macro*-damage it is clear that the *micro*-damage produced by the single impact is of interest as the initiating cause. As will
be shown, at a sufficiently high speed, the damage done by collision
with a single water drop is surprisingly extensive and severe. Elaborate
theories have been developed in connection with the impact by drops or
spheres and there exists a formidable bibliography, but here we are concerned entirely with a descriptive account and essentially with an
illustration of new information revealed by interferometric methods.

It was, of course, anticipated that marked differences might be
expected between impacts on and by metals and plastics. In any case
the high speeds are responsible for the propagations of transient disturbances so that elastic wave propagation can be expected to play
a big part. In our experiments an air gun was designed to fire either the
cylindrical projectiles or the spheres. As these would be lethal at the
velocities used, special protective precautions had to be taken. Four
interchangeable gun barrels were employed with diameters from $\frac{11}{64}$ in.
to $\frac{17}{64}$ in. They had smooth bores and were screwed to an air chamber
which could be pumped to a pressure of 300 lb/in.^{2}. On firing, the pro-

jectiles could attain a maximum speed of 480 metres/sec when maximum pressure was used. The various projectiles were : (a) steel ball-bearings ; (b) polished glass spheres ; (c) lead shot ; (d) polythene pellets. These were the materials shot into the plates. For firing at suspended water drops flat-end cylinders of aluminium and of Perspex were used. Velocities were measured by a determination of the time of flight across a short measured track, the projectile interrupting in succession two light beams illuminating photo-cells, and the time of passage was given from a timing trigger circuit. Ballistic pendulum experiments subsequently confirmed the correctness of the timing system.

Impacts on Perspex. Since Perspex suffers great damage in rainstorms, impact on Perspex was first examined. Using steel balls, and in the relatively lower velocity range (up to 100 m/s) impact on a Perspex sheet leads to the formation of an annular depressed region surrounded by circular ring cracks. It appears that the classical Hertz theory for elastic deformation can be fitted to the observations. This seems to be true for impact by glass spheres and also for impact on aluminium as well as on Perspex. It was with the polythene pellet impacts that we first secured phenomena which resemble the rain-erosion effects suffered by aircraft. It was found convenient in some experiments to use polythene pellets, short cylinders with hemispherical ends of radius of curvature 2·5 mm and of total mass 1/20th g.

Plate 307 (× 14) is a typical interferogram of the collision pit produced by impact of polythene on Perspex sheet at a velocity of 330 m/s (685 miles per hour). There is much of interest on this photograph. Proceeding from the centre outwards it establishes that the central region is reasonably flat. This is then surrounded by an annular depression (fringes of equal chromatic order were used to show which is the up and which the down). This depression is some 4 waves deep. Around it is a very extensive region of fractured crack marks. The cracks are mainly circular and concentric, although at times they do cross. The way in which the crack region fades out is well established by following the fringes to the undisturbed regions. The amplitudes of the cracks are also obtainable from the fringe pattern.

Careful examination reveals that the profile of the cracks is that of an alternating saw-tooth. Heights near the edge of the depression certainly exceed half a light wave as is evidenced from the gradual growth in amplitude from outwards towards the centre. The crack amplitudes appear to alternate large and small, but the general break up of the surface makes it impossible to secure exact data inside the heavily cracked regions. Plate 308 (× 35) is a micrograph giving a vivid im-

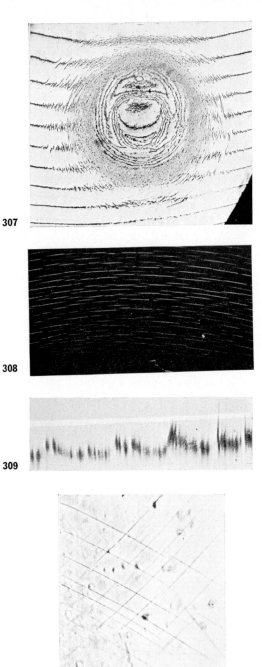

307

308

309

310

Plates 307-310

pression of the complexity of part of the crack region. Fringes of equal chromatic order, taken along a radial section, well away from the centre and in a region of only slight crack amplitude, are shown at higher magnification ($\times$ 200) in Plate 309. This shows clearly the zig-zag saw-tooth character and indicates that there is secondary minor amplitude cracking between the main crack peaks. In this particular picture high dispersion is used, but the amplitude can readily be inferred by comparing the crack heights with the fringe *width*. For, as the fringe width itself approximates to some 50 Å, it is clear that the major crack amplitude in this particular instance, is some 200 Å. (No especial significance is to be attached to this, as the amplitude depends entirely upon the region selected for interferometric examination. The matter is raised here merely as an illustration of the fact that small displacements in fringes of equal chromatic order can always be assessed even from *one* fringe using the fringe *width* as a measure of dispersion.)

As Plate 310 ($\times$ 300) shows, crack regions can intersect, hence it is not surprising that the fringes are intensely ragged in the heavily cracked regions. In effect this micro-break-up, which penetrates into the body of the material, is a surface roughening. This leads optically to considerable diffraction and scatter of light as a result of which full development of the build-up of multiple-beams is prevented. The fringes therefore lose their individuality in the strongly crazed regions.

This cracking may possibly arise from the tensile stresses produced by the displaced material caused by the central depression. However, their sharpness and curved character, associated with the intersection effects, seem to point to a shock-wave propagation cause. Measurements were made of the diameters of the cracked regions as a function of the impacting velocity in the range 200 to 430 metres per second. In this range, the diameter D was related to the velocity V approximately in the relation D is proportional to $V^{1 \cdot 6}$. The diameters of the depressions did not increase so rapidly but were found to be proportional to $V^{1 \cdot 2}$. Hence at the higher speeds the proportion of crazed area to depression area increases steadily. Thus in a given instance, at 400 m/s the crazed diameter was 6 mm whilst the depression diameter was only 2·8 mm. The crazed area is then some $3\frac{1}{2}$ times the area of the central depression.

From the fringe pattern, the volume of the depression itself can be reasonably closely assessed. From a value of 8×10^{-8} cm³ at a velocity of 230 m/s it increases rapidly to as much as 950×10^{-8} cm³ at 400 m/s. To a rough approximation we find the surprising result that the volume of the depression is actually proportional to V^8, an unusually high power-law. It is this high power-law which surely explains the rapid fierce increase in damage as the velocity of an aircraft increases.

The violence of the surface cracking led one to suspect that the cracks must penetrate appreciably into the body of the material. Some specimens subject to impact at 400 m/s were sectioned and it was established that the cracks went down to a depth of some 0·09 mm. This is enormous compared with the heights of the surface deformations, which were measured in ångström units. Exactly as in the formation of ring cracks on diamond, a small surface distortion hides a far larger interior amount of damage. As there, it can be inferred that even a *micro*-surface defect is associated with a *macro*-internal defect within the body of the material. It is not surprising that the successive repeated impact in a rainstorm can lead to serious break-up of the structure of the material.

Impacts on Duraluminium. Although duraluminium is difficult to polish well for interferometry, the effects observed were on a sufficiently big scale such that the evident lack of polish did not interfere seriously with the interferometric studies. The first important difference found between the metal and Perspex was that no appreciable depression could be made on the metal with a polythene pellet of velocity below 330 m/s, a fact which restricted very much the available velocity range for study with this material. Interferograms found for 380 m/s impacts of polythene on duraluminium revealed reasonably symmetric, flat-base, shallow depressions, for which volume estimates could be made. Over the admittedly small velocity range of 330 to 450 m/s the volume of the depression is proportional to $V^{9·7}$. This still higher index power-law explains the rapid vanishing of any effect below a velocity of 330 m/s. It can only be regarded as a rough approximation.

The interferograms enable one to establish that on duraluminium the depressions are reasonably spherical caps. This would imply that at these velocities the indentation process even with a material as soft as polythene is in fact similar to the indentation produced by a hard metal ball. But there is a very considerable deformation effect on the polythene. For the radius of curvature of the indent, as given by the fringes is some 10 cm. But the radius of curvature of the polythene hemisphere was only 0·25 cm, which is forty times as curved as the indent. Both the considerable deformation of the pellet and perhaps some elastic recovery of the metal have contributed to this. It should be noted that the $V^{9·7}$ law relates velocity with the *recovered* indentation. As the law of recovery is quite unknown for high-velocity impact, and since in fact the actual indentation is very slight, it is evident that

at lower velocities the indent may even be largely elastic with propor-
tionate very considerable relative recovery. Clearly the 9·7 index has
very little physical meaning until these various effects can be sorted out.
All that can safely be inferred is that it is the final recovered volumes
which increase rapidly with velocity above 330 m/s. This is by no
means a trivial conclusion, for this is the aspect of practical importance
in connection with the aircraft rain-erosion problems.

The V^8 law found for Perspex, since it was extended over a much
bigger velocity range than was the case of the duraluminium, is less
likely to be so seriously at fault, yet here too must be borne in mind the
existence of an elastic recovery. In both instances it is necessary to
treat with caution the numerical value of the index in the power-laws
found. What is quite certain is that these indices cannot as yet receive
a physical interpretation.

Impacts on Suspended Water Drops. A drop of water of some 2 mm
diameter was suspended on a fine fibre and at this was fired a flat-ended
cylindrical specimen. After the impact the specimen entered a large
box lightly filled with cotton wool and was slowed down and stopped
without suffering any detectable damage in the process. The rear ends
of the specimens had grooves in them which prevented yawing. Perspex
samples were used in the first experiments and as their mass was some
200 mg, transfer of momentum can be disregarded since the drop itself
weighed some 4 mg only. The supporting fibres were extremely fine and
no complications due to the fibre could be noticed. Indeed the fibres
may well have been blown away by the projectile before the collision
took place. Before firing, the flat end of the Perspex was polished and
after the impact it was silvered and studied interferometrically. Plate
311 (× 30) shows the appearance of the indent on Perspex produced at
330 m/s, using oblique shadowing illumination to heighten the contrast.
An interferogram is shown in Plate 312 (× 50). This contains a good
deal of information. (It is of some interest to draw attention to the
two long scratch marks on the sample. These have nothing to do with
the collision, but were scratch-mark residues from polishing and hand-
ling. Yet in fact these scratch marks are in themselves useful and
instructive, especially that running through the diameter of the indent.
For some parts of the pattern are elevations and some are depressions
and the directions of the kinks within the scratch mark are actually tell-
tale indicators of which regions are up and which down.)

In the main, the pattern consists of a central feature surrounded by
extensive crack marks. A schematic profile is shown in Plate 313. The
scale is magnified 40 times in extension, but 10,000 times in vertical

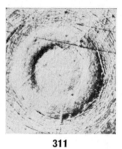

311

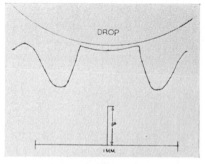

DROP

1 M.M.

313

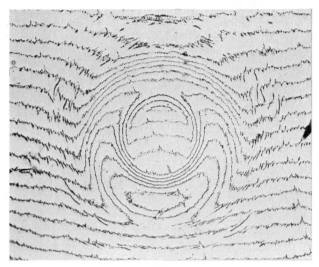

312

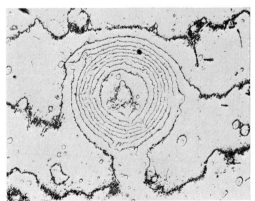

314

Plates 311-314

scale, for the vertical line represents 1 micron and is near enough 1 cm long. The vertical scale is then 250 times the horizontal scale on this diagram. The diameter of the drop is about twice the width of the crack pattern shown. The pattern is somewhat unexpected.

With measurements made with impact velocities ranging from 230 to 450 m/s again a rough V^8 law is found for the relation between velocity and volume of indent. But the crazing effect produced by water is invariably *much less marked* than that produced by the polythene. This is well shown up by comparing the two interferograms Plates 307 and 312.

We were unable to induce effects on duraluminium with a water drop because the mass of the metal pellet only enabled us to reach a velocity of 330 m/s. As already indicated this is the lower limit for producing any effect at all on duraluminium. To secure some information of the behaviour on a comparable metal it was necessary to substitute aluminium (which is appreciably softer) for the harder duraluminium. With this softer metal, indentations appeared against a water drop at the relatively low speed of 230 m/s. The range 230–330 m/s was therefore available for interferometric study and in this range excellent indents were obtained. Plate 314 ($\times$ 40) shows the maximum effect we could produce, at the top available speed of 330 m/s. It is certainly possible to conclude from the shape of the indent that the water drop has not broken up but retained some kind of pseudo-spherical shape during the collision. Indeed, it is behaving effectively like a metal sphere. The fringe pattern is closely enough that given by a spherical cap. Over the range available the law for the increase in volume of indent with increasing velocity was found to be $V^{8\cdot9}$ which is close to the laws already described for water impact with Perspex and for polythene impact, both with Perspex and with duraluminium.

Once more the radius of curvature for the indent differs markedly from that of the drop. It ranges from 35 to 55 mm according to the velocity of impact, whilst the radius of the drop itself was only 1 mm. It is doubtful if so big an increase in the radius can be accounted for by recovery. It is almost certain that the drop flattens considerably at impact so that the long radius of curvature is a measure of the radius of curvature taken up by the deformed drop. The full detailed interpretation must await further experimentation.

It is of interest to mention that if an impacted Perspex sheet is heated for half an hour to a temperature of 140° C the annular depression so characteristic, and shown in Plate 313, recovers and nearly vanishes. This is strong evidence that the annular depression is not produced by the actual *removal* of material by the impact (i.e. there is no real loss) but is largely an elastic deformation ' frozen-in ' and recovering back on heating. Because of this observation, impact experiments both with steel balls and with polythene balls were made on Perspex sheet maintained at different temperatures. The temperature range covered was $- 100°$ C to $+ 140°$ C. It is of interest to report that at 140° C the crazed region still appears, but there is no effective central depression. One can argue that the central depression formed at the instant of impact but then immediately recovered. The low-temperature results do not differ materially from those found at room temperature.

Any creep effect on the patterns produced at room temperature can be completely disregarded, for a specimen of Perspex fired at a water drop was found to have retained its pattern unchanged after a lapse of four months.

REFERENCES

Letters M, X, Y.

21. DIRECTIONAL ABRASION RESISTANCE ON DIAMOND

Micro-abrasion testing of diamond—Resistance on the dodecahedral plane—References.

SINCE the Middle Ages it has been known traditionally that diamond offers different resistance to grinding and polishing in different directions. This is why diamond, the hardest material, can be polished into a brilliant gemstone by diamond powder. The harder directions, in which some powder particles must be oriented, attack the selected softer directions on the diamond being polished. Empirical knowledge accumulated, and it was known to the early lapidaries that certain planes were easier to cut and polish than others. Furthermore it was soon discovered that on these planes there were both easier and harder *directions* of polish. Certain directions, called grain directions, were found to be highly resistant, and at right angles to these grain directions the rate of polishing was fastest. These grain directions were recognized by their crystallographic orientation relative to the crystal edges. Despite centuries of accumulation of tradition, some contradictory, no serious study scientifically of the differential rates of grinding in different directions appears to have been undertaken until Tolkowski (D.Sc. Thesis, London University, 1920) took up the matter. He abraded diamonds under standardized conditions and determined rates of removal of material by weighing. He reported that the rate of removal was proportional to the velocity of the grinding wheel. It was also proportional to the applied load, up to a certain critical value, after which rate of removal was independent of load. The various grain directions were studied. On the *cubic plane two* easy grinding directions were found. On the *dodecahedron plane* he reports *one* easy direction, and this was twice as fast as the easy cubic directions. He was *unable*, under his standardized conditions, to grind the *octahedron* plane itself at all. Grinding was, however, possible for a direction *slightly off* the true octahedron plane and on such a plane *three* easy directions were found. It is those particles in the diamond grinding dust which are set along the hard octahedron direction which enable grinding of other faces to be carried out.

After Tolkowski, much further work has been carried out in this field, especially by Slawson (numerous papers in *Amer. Mineralogist*, 1939 to 1950), who has developed successful crystallographic theories for the properties of the various grinding directions. He established that grinding is easiest in directions parallel to the crystallographic axes. One quite unexpected effect found was the existence of a *vector* hardness effect which has the following character. Taking an easy grinding direction, then it is found that along this direction grinding is easier for a wheel rotating in one sense, than in the opposite sense, i.e. the *direction of motion* contributes to some extent.

In all of this experimental work the removal of complete areas and facets is involved, with the result that average data only are obtained. A method was thereupon developed by P. Grodzinski and A. Stern (*Nature*, **164**, 193, 1949) for carrying out micro-abrasions on diamond which enable quite small local resistances to abrasion to be determined. Such an approach was desirable since several older authorities on diamond (see A. F. Williams, *Genesis of Diamond*, London, 1932) had long maintained that different diamonds vary in their abrasion resistance. More to the point is the fact well known to the lapidary that on a single diamond, regions of high resistance can often be encountered. Whether the cause is twinning, or distortion, the fact of the variation is of practical importance and therefore certainly justifies the development of a method which permits such local variations on a diamond to be measured, apart from the intrinsic interest of determining variation with crystallographic direction. The method to be described is an abrasion resistance hardness test and not an indentation hardness test.

The machine, made by Grodzinski, produces very small grinding marks and to evaluate these correctly it is really necessary to determine their volumes. It is at this point that multiple-beam interferometry comes into the picture. We have therefore made studies on diamonds using Grodzinski's own machine for the purpose and these will now be described.

Micro-abrasion Testing of Diamond

The Grodzinski machine consists of a 1-in. diameter iron wheel, the rim of which is ground to a conical sharp edge of included angle 110°. This wheel, on specially designed vibration-free mountings, is driven at high speed, some 10,000 revolutions per minute, and is charged with a suspension of diamond powder in oil. The diamond is brought up to the wheel on a light balanced arm and weights applied, such that a bearing

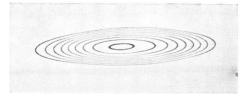

315

316

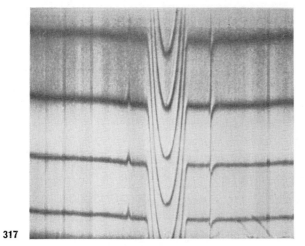

317

Plates 315-317

load of 75 g presses the diamond against the rotating conical wheel. This is run for a fixed time, the actual number of revolutions to which the diamond is subject being given by an automatic counter. In carrying out experiments with diamond it is found that frequent regrinding of the conical edge is necessary.

Grinding time was usually less than a minute and the cuts which were made varied in length from 0·2 to 0·7 mm. In width they never exceeded 0·15 mm. Such small cuts permit of local variations and variations with direction to be studied on average sized diamonds. The interferometric approach, as will appear shortly, turns out to be ideal for the cut dimensions encountered. Furthermore, in some instances extremely shallow effects are produced (on resistant faces) and indeed only multiple-beam interferometry can give any useful information in such cases. Abrasion experiments were made on cubic, dodecahedron and octahedron planes, using good gem quality crystals. As usual in our precision surface studies, it was necessary to section and polish cubic planes and dodecahedron planes, but the octahedron planes studied were natural planes on good portrait stones. The shapes of the abrasion cuts as given interferometrically will now be discussed.

Plate 315 (× 100) shows a reflection interferogram, with high definition, for an abrasion cut made on a cubic face. On the crystal itself, the cut length is only half a millimetre. The depth and shape are readily assessed from the fringe pattern and by using reasonable approximations the volume removed can be computed. The perfection of polish within the abrasion cut is most striking, the extreme fringe sharpness revealing this feature. This can be seen further to advantage in the interferogram for another cut shown at double the magnification in Plate 316 (× 200). A further point, clear in this picture, is the complete absence of any distortion or pile-up edge effect. The cut is very sharp and the edge abrupt.

An abrasion attempted in a hard direction can be very shallow, and to assess such a shallow cut, the use of fringes of equal chromatic order is advisable. Plate 317 (× 140) shows such fringes taken diametrically across the central short axis of one such cut. The fringes show the true profile and the maximum depth to be some 2·75 orders. The advantage of this fringe system is that the exact depth is given without any uncertainty (there can be some uncertain guesswork in allowing for the central fractional order in monochromatic Fizeau fringes). Again it will be noticed that there is complete absence of edge pile-up ; for this fringe system, with its high dispersion, is particularly suited for showing up even an extremely small pile-up effect. The very real advantage of the fringes of equal chromatic order is revealed when a shallow abrasion is to be examined. Plate 318 (× 350) which is a high-magnification, and high-interferometric-dispersion, picture (120,000 times magnification in height) shows admirably the cross-sectional shape for a shallow abrasion cut which is about 3200 Å deep. Here once more the complete absence of surface distortion is established and the shape of the cut is excellently demonstrated. Although the included angle on the wheel was 110°, the sides of the cuts have much shallower slopes, for the included angle is some 176° on Plate 316 for instance. The sides only dip some 2° away from the horizontal. Clearly the abrasion is being produced effectively by a rounded tip, whether due to tip geometry or to elastic flattening is as yet not established.

The result of a directional vector test made on a cubic plane is illustrated by the interferogram on Plate 319 (× 30). This picture shows the whole cubic face so that the crystal directions are clear. The abrasions have been made along the directions of the diagonals of the square face obtained by truncating an octahedron. They are the classic *easy* directions. Four abrasions under identical load and speed conditions have been made along one diagonal and four along the other. However, the wheel was alternately rotated one way and then reversed. Without any detailed numerical analysis it is clear that a true vector effect is shown. For the cuts alternate long and short, as the wheel is reversed. Thus in the best direction, parallel to the crystal axis, the two favourable long cuts have lengths 3·6 and 3·1 microns. But on reversing the wheel, yet along the same axis, the two cuts have lengths only 2·1 and 1·6 microns. Again in the direction at right angles to this two parallel cuts in the same sense have lengths 3·9 and 2·7 microns, whilst wheel reversal leads to values of 2·3 and 1·4 microns. These experiments were continued over a complete range of orientations. They establish without any doubt at all that on the cubic face there are two easy directions, at right angles to each other, but in addition there is a clearly marked very real directional vector effect too. We thus confirm on a micro-scale the general findings on a macro-scale of both Tolkowski and of Slawson. But it is noteworthy that there are very real local differences on different parts of the same crystal, since none of the four equivalent pairs are anywhere identical. There is no question about the reality of the gross difference due to vector effect, but it would seem that there are certainly local variations. This is not surprising for local crystallographic defects are bound to have important secondary effects on local abrasive resistances.

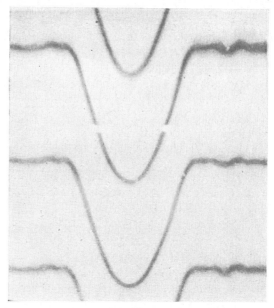

318

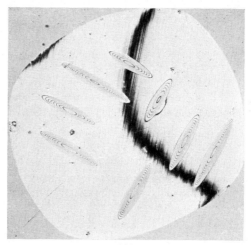

319

Plates 318, 319

Directional Resistance on the Dodecahedral Plane

Studies were made on a dodecahedral plane, but unfortunately the plane available was but crudely polished. (One is often in the hands of an industrial polishing organization which treats requests for odd polished faces for scientific purposes as rather interfering with its normal industrial practice. This can lead to very long delays and one must then be content with second best surfaces, or suffer an abnormal delay. For a research student working for a higher degree this reluctantly imposes the necessity of using an inferior surface at times. The dodecahedron surface studied here was in such a category.) The crudeness of the polish does not seriously affect the investigations reported here, it merely complicates the overall interference pattern, not the abrasion marks.

Plate 320 ($\times$ 24) shows the surface of the stone studied, and on it no less than eight abrasion marks have been attempted. The surface is half a mm. long and retains the crude saw marks which the polisher has not fully removed. All that has been done by the polisher was a general smoothing. The alternate ridges shown by the fringes are usual on freshly sawn faces. Four abrasion cuts have been made parallel to the short axis of the face and four parallel to the long axis. Yet *only four* abrasion cuts have materialized. The four (vertical) patterns, parallel to the short axis, are quite clear in Plate 320, but those *attempted* under identical conditions parallel to the long axis are not visible.

This then first establishes the existence of only *one* easy direction on the dodecahedron face, and once more we are in agreement with Tolkowski.

However, here on the dodecahedral face we establish now that there is *practically no detectable vector direction effect*. For on Plate 321 ($\times$ 80) are the two abrasion cuts in the one direction (on the left in Plate 320, and parallel to the crystal axis), whilst in Plate 322 ($\times$ 80) are shown the pair secured when the wheel was reversed. There is little to choose between these two sets, certainly not enough to establish the existence of any genuine vector effect. On the contrary these show that any such vector effect must be small, if it exists at all.

On another crystal we did succeed in making a slight abrasion in the *unfavourable* direction perpendicular to the favourable direction which was shown in Plate 320. These cuts in the unfavourable sense, two of them, were very shallow, the one 960 Å and the other 750 Å deep. The fringes of equal chromatic order across these are shown in Plate 323 ($\times$ 100). Attention must be drawn to the fact that these may in part

320

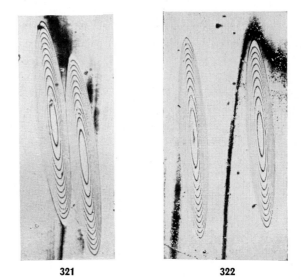

321   322

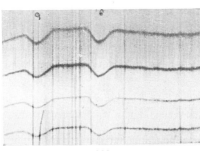

323

Plates 320-323

be spurious. For if the polished plane is not truly dodecahedral and is appreciably *off* the true plane, then one can anticipate a partial reduction of resistance in the *un*favourable direction. Just as it is possible to abrade a plane slightly off octahedral, so it will be possible to abrade slightly in the *un*favourable direction on a plane slightly off the dodecahedral. Plate 323 must not be accepted at all as establishing a second direction on the dodecahedral plane, since no X-ray determination of orientation was carried out at the time the experiment was made to ascertain the true orientation of the face abraded. The face had been selected by eye by the polisher and may well have been a few degrees off true, probably was. The abrasion effect in Plate 323 is so slight compared with that in Plate 321 (say 960 Å compared with 30,000 Å) that it can be disregarded from the *practical* point of view, even if it is not spurious. We therefore conclude that there is but one easy direction on the dodecahedron and no effective vector effect.

Finally, in agreement with Tolkowski again, no impression at all could be made on the octahedron faces of diamonds. Even with the most sensitive multiple-beam interference technique no depression could be detected on the octahedral faces abraded. Our general conclusions can be summarized as follows :

(*a*) The cubic face has two easy grinding directions, parallel to the crystallographic axes.

(*b*) There is a marked vector effect, possibly in the ratio of some 2 : 1 roughly.

(*c*) The dodecahedron face has only one easy direction, parallel to the crystallographic axis. This direction is also easier than the easy cubic directions.

(*d*) There is no noticeable vector effect on the dodecahedron face.

(*e*) Faint impressions can be made on a dodecahedron at right angles to the easy direction, but this may be due to being off the true dodecahedral plane in the experiments made and must not be accepted without further investigation.

(*f*) No abrasions can be made on the octahedron face.

(*g*) The polish within the abrasions is very high.

(*h*) There is no ploughing or pile-up effect whatsoever, outside of the abrasion mark.

With regard to (*e*) it should be noted that there was a distinct difference in the abrasion speed on the favourable dodecahedral direction between two separately prepared dodecahedral surfaces. The one dodecahedral plane was set by eye, the other set by X-rays, and the latter was the faster. Clearly this indicates that a slight deviation from the true plane can vitiate observation and shows that future studies on abrasion must require critical X-ray orientation of the faces abraded. We have in this observation a possible explanation of the fact that lapidaries have constantly maintained that there is only *one* easy direction on the cubic plane, whereas Tolkowski, Slawson, Denning and ourselves, find that there are *two*. Clearly if the stone is misoriented the one direction will be easier than the other, and lapidaries grinding by hand and eye without X-rays and without critical mechanical adjustment of the stone are bound, in general, to be somewhat off the true plane. They will indeed find one direction easier than the other, but with a critically correct setting they should find two equally easy directions.

REFERENCES

Nos. 26, G.

22. POLISH AND SAWING OF DIAMOND

The polish of diamond—The finish of sawn diamond References.

The Polish of Diamond

GEMSTONE diamonds have a characteristically fine and brilliant polish which is accentuated in appearance by the high reflectivity. It has often been stated that the facets of brilliants are flat, but in fact it can be demonstrated interferometrically that this is not the case unless exceptionable trouble is taken. A so-called optically ' flat ' diamond, although it was a mere 5 mm square, prepared commercially by standard high-quality diamond industrial polishing methods, was found to deviate from the flat by more than $\lambda/4$ and was covered by a regular array of deep polish scratches. A deviation of $\lambda/4$ for so small an area means a considerable departure from the usual conception of an optical flat.

Some experiments have been made to test the optical finish to be expected in a reasonable polishing time using industrial polishing methods. (The time factor is what matters, for, given long enough, it is always possible to push the finish further and further.) The progress in polishing was followed interferometrically. The surface selected for polishing was the easy cubic plane and was a mere 3×3 mm square. Plate 324 ($\times$ 20) shows this surface as received from a well-known industrial polishing firm which supplied the surface as a high grade flat. Of course they did not have multiple-beam interferometry to assist. The errors are self evident, but the polish scratches are not too deep.

We then repolished this surface on a cast-iron scaife driven at 2850 revolutions per minute. The polishing material was a fine diamond powder of size less than 1 micron. After some hours the result obtained is shown by the interferogram in Plate 325 ($\times$ 20). The curvature has been considerably reduced, but there still remains some polish scratch micro-detail. Again a repolish was undertaken, but this time a wooden scaife was used and the diamond was mechanically oscillated whilst the scaife rotated. The ultimate polish after some further hours was that given by the interferogram on Plate 326 ($\times$ 20). This surface still exhibits residual curvature and the fine grain polish scratches still persist.

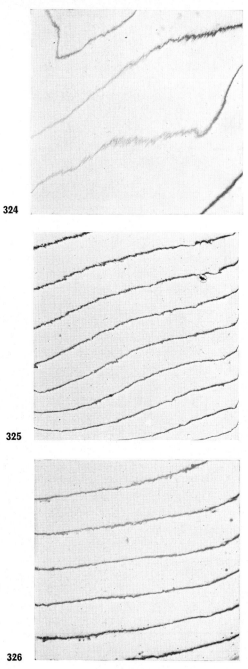

324

325

326

Plates 324-326

It will be noticed that the finish is a good deal inferior to that shown within the abrasion marks, such as those on Plates 315, 316, 318. It may well be that the difference is due to speed of rotation, since the abrasive used was not very different in the two cases. Alternatively the relatively very low applied load when making the abrasions may have contributed. The matter deserves further study.

Considering the small area involved in the preparation of the flat surface shown in Plate 326 it seems clear that diamond cannot be polished as well as glass can be.

The Finish of Sawn Diamond

In this brief section a description will be given of a few observations made on the finish of *sawn* diamond. Interferometry reveals that the finish is remarkably good in parts and indicates that undoubtedly the sawing action is accompanied by a polishing action. Sawing plays a very important role in the fabrication of diamond and its introduction in the late nineteenth century revolutionized machining processes and rates of production of shaped diamonds, whether for gems or tools. The saws used are thin circular blades clamped between solid discs to increase stiffness. They are rotated at very high speeds. As a rule a cream of oil and diamond dust is fed on to the blade and the diamond to be cut allowed to rest on the blade, effectively loaded by a gravity feed. Sawing is quite slow and it may take some hours to go through a small stone. In practice a long bank of rotating machines is set up and the oil-diamond cream is replenished at intervals, which may well be half-hourly.

When a sawn surface is examined interferometrically it shows an alternating succession of ragged regions and smoother regions. We find that the number of such regions seems to correspond with the half-hourly replenishments of diamond dust. Plate 327 ($\times$ 35) is a composite picture which shows such typical alternations of rugosities on moving across the sawn face. This type of picture, of which we have many, would strongly suggest that traditional practice should be modified so as to incorporate a *continuous feed* of diamond dust rather than the manual *intermittent* feed. For this is more likely to lead to a more uniform finish on the sawn work. Clearly the more uniform the sawn finish the less the labour involved in the final polishing.

We have found that at times sawn regions are surprisingly smooth, especially when one considers the rough character of the sawing mechanism. Some high dispersion fringes on a selected good-quality sawn region of a cubic plane are shown in Plate 328 ($\times$ 170). First, it

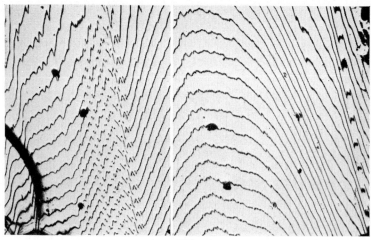

327

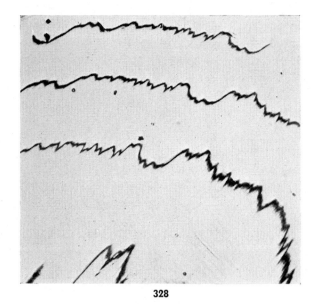

328

Plates 327, 328

will be noticed that the general surface structure is good. Secondly, it is clear that there is an oriented secondary polish structure which is on quite a small scale. There is little doubt that the sawing process acts at the same time as a polishing mechanism. Doubtless the finer diamond particles are embedded in the rotating disc, and because of the high speed the grinding is linked with polishing.

REFERENCES

Letters G, V.

23. THE WEAR OF GLAZIER'S DIAMONDS

Polished-edge glazier's diamonds—Natural cutting edges—References.

As an extension of our purely scientific studies on cleavage and percussion of diamond we have initiated investigations into the wear of industrial diamond cutting tools using interferometric methods. It is intended to study both lathe cutting tools and drills, especially rock boring drills which are subject to such severe wear, but a beginning has been made on the much gentler wear processes encountered by the edges of the glazier's glass cutting diamond. Two kinds of glazier's diamond cutting tool are in use, those which use a diamond with a *polished* cutting edge and those in which a diamond has been selected with a *natural* sharp curved edge resulting from the intersection of curved faces, which can meet at quite sharp edges. These might be dodecahedron faces, but even more so are those edges arising through octahedral faces developing into trisoctahedral type in which the octahedron face grows to a pyramidal centre which is a fine point, a natural edge usually very resistant to wear.

Polished cutting edges are usually not straight but curved. The angle subtended by the two faces meeting at the cutting edge may be of the order of 140°. Tradition has it that a *natural* edge survives wear in use far longer than a polished edge, but is usually considered not to be as sharp as a polished edge. Much work has been reported on the *widths* of the cuts made on glass but a study of their *depths* has had to await a multiple-beam approach, for the cuts are very shallow indeed. A good cut for glass breaking is considered that which has a width not exceeding 30 microns. A bad cut splinters sideways to a considerable extent and can show a width of even 200 microns. Effectively the good cut goes *downwards* and the bad cut spreads *sideways*.

We have discussed with skilled glass cutters the type of load and the speed of cutting action which they consider to be most advantageous and conclude from the subjective impressions of the experts that some 500 g is likely to be a good load, although there is some difficulty in estimating this. It is much easier to estimate the speed of hand movement in the cut made by the long-experienced operatives, and their best speeds appear to be of the order of 1 metre per second (say 200 ft per minute) or a little less. These data served as a guiding starting point for our experiments.

An examination of thirty *polished* glazier's cutters which had received prolonged heavy industrial use, showed that these worn tools had in common broad serrated edges which were crossed with numerous cracks, on a micro-scale, running perpendicularly to the cutting edge. It was considered desirable to secure a continuous record of wear under closely controlled conditions and the following experimental approach was adopted. A diamond was set on the bed of an automatic lathe, a load applied and a long continuous helical cut turned spiral fashion on to a long glass cylinder of diameter 4 in. A thread-cutting lathe was used for the operation, set to cut 300 threads to the inch. Experiments were made with diamonds which were loaded respectively with 400 g and with 500 g, at speeds of 85 ft and 150 ft per minute, which happened to be available on the particular lathe being used.

On a 2 ft long cylinder a continuous cut $1\frac{1}{2}$ miles long would be made. In some of our experiments we have continued the cut with a single edge on to ten such cylinders, covering a total cutting length of *15 miles* (i.e. 24 km). We have found that the glass effectively moulds itself to the shape of the diamond so that the shape of the continuous cut becomes a record of the sharpness of the diamond edge. It is necessary to reveal the shape of the cut by precision interferometry. As the cutting edge deteriorates so the shape of the cut progressively changes. After the full length cut of $1\frac{1}{2}$ miles has been made, the glass cylinder is cut up into short lengths and pieces are selected, silvered and examined by multiple-beam interferometry. So a continuous record of the behaviour of the diamond cutting edge is secured. Some observations made on polished-edge glazier's diamonds will first be considered.

Polished-edge Glazier's Diamonds

The detailed examination of the deterioration of the edge of one diamond after cutting for 3 miles is as follows. A microphotograph of the edge of the fresh diamond is shown in Plate 329 (× 270). It was loaded with 500 g and a cut made $1\frac{1}{2}$ miles in length (2·4 km). The appearance of the edge after this cut is that shown in Plate 330 (× 270). The cut was continued until it was 3 miles long (4·8 km) and the edge appearance at this stage was that shown in Plate 331 (× 370). It is clear that the edge breaks down into serrations which increase in extent with the wear.

The interferogram made at the beginning of the operation is shown in Plate 332 × (110). As the topography of a cylinder is under examination,

329   330   331

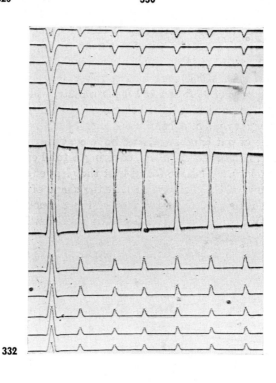

332

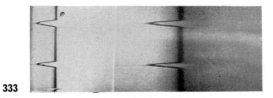

333

Plates 329-333

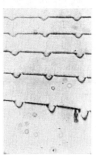
334

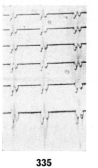
335

336

337

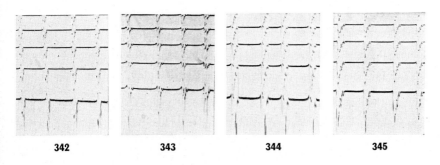
338

339

340

341

342

343

344

345

Plates 334-345

the fringes are more or less straight lines with cut kinks in them, running parallel to the cylinder axis. The dispersion for successive orders obeys the same law as for Newton's rings, i.e. the radii are proportional to the square roots of the natural whole numbers. A fringe displacement towards the centre indicates a hollow.

Although the diamond was placed gently on to the moving cylinder there is a definite initial kinetic effect and the first cut, at the left, is anomalously broad and deep, yet still very sharp. Thereafter the early cuts are all extremely uniform and all are nearly 1000 Å deep. There are numerous interesting features visible in these fringes. First there is virtually no pile-up at all at the edges, although slight pile-up is detectable on the first anomalous kinetically influenced cut. Second, the fringes (on the lower half of the picture especially) show clear evidence of secondary micro-cracking within the cuts. For the sides are distinctly serrated. In particular there is a real fracture at the base. Third, although the width of the cut is uniformly 17·5 microns the depth is a mere 1000 Å. The sides therefore slope inwards *at the very small angle of only 36 minutes of arc* (interferometric magnification is great in depth). Two of the cuts are shown with fringes of equal chromatic order in Plate 333 (also × 110). The left-hand fringe shows that there is a fracture on the side of the cut in both cases.

In Plates 334, 335, 336 and 337 (all at × 100) are shown successively the fringe patterns after cut lengths respectively of 170 m, 1·2 km, 2·4 km, 4·8 km. To our surprise we found that the very sharp V-shaped cut with which the system started lasted *only 100 metres*, thereafter it became cup-shaped as in Plate 334. Continued cutting leads to the appearance of multiple cupping as seen in Plate 335. This is obviously clearly related to the development of the serrations shown on Plate 330. As wear develops the multiple character becomes more extensive and the cut becomes deeper and broader and very ragged.

The initial sharpness of the fresh cutting edge plays an important role. One of our polished diamonds had a particularly sharp narrow cutting edge and Plates 338 to 345 (all × 110) illustrate the performance of this exceptional edge. The total cutting length covered in these eight interferograms is only 1500 metres and the behaviour is of interest. It was initially very sharp and narrow and as such was fragile. The breakdown was therefore rapid and spectacular. Although the standard load and speed was used, the initial early cuts, shown in Plate 338, were twice as deep and only half as wide as the initial cut in the former example. The cuts start off with a 2000-Å depth and a 9-micron width. The slope-in of the sides approximates some 2°. Plate 339 corresponds to

33 m and the cuts are still good and sharp. Plate 340 is for 66 m and already irregularities are appearing. At 120 m, on Plate 341, serious anomalies are appearing. Local fractures appear and some very noticeable asymmetric pile-up can be seen. By 500 m, Plate 342, the edge has broken down, and the serrated complexity develops further for the next three plates, which are respectively for 800, 1200 and 1500 m.

Although the initial V-shape persists to 170 m, rounding of the apex already sets in at 66 m. There is asymmetrical pile-up in all cuts beyond 120 m. The broken pattern of the cut found at the end of the track can always be fitted to the shape of the diamond as observed at the end, which proves that the intermediate patterns are true mouldings of the shape of the diamond at their particular lengths of cut. It is evident from this that there is an optimum sharpness. *Too sharp an edge is too fragile and gives a short life.*

Natural Cutting Edges

A glazier's diamond with a *natural* (unpolished) dodecahedron cutting edge is shown in Plate 346 (× 270). After a run of *no less than 24 km* the edge had the appearance shown in Plate 347 (× 270). Although a series of small parallel cracks have appeared, running perpendicularly *across* the cutting edge, the final total width of the damaged edge is less than that of a polished edge which has cut only 4·8 km. This is in complete accord with traditional opinion on the superior life of the natural edge. The interferograms given by the natural edge are of some interest.

A sequence of such interferograms for the cuts given by the natural edge is shown in Plates 348 to 353 (all at × 110). The performance is surprisingly different to that of the polished edge. The initial cut at the start of the operation, Plate 348, is narrow *but multiple*, with breaks on the sides. It has the character of a typical 500 m cut from a polished edge. The next interferogram, Plate 349, is for 2500 m and by this time some definite rounding and cupping has set in. Plate 350 is for 3·2 km, and there is surprisingly little change. Plate 351 is for 4·8 km, Plate 352 for 14·4 km and Plate 353 for 24 km.

It is clear that although the natural edge starts off at a considerable disadvantage compared with the polished edge yet it maintains itself far longer. Indeed the 15-mile pattern, although wide and multiple, is in the class of the 4500-ft pattern of a polished edge. Our findings therefore amply confirm tradition and show that a much longer life is to be expected from the natural edge. On the other hand it is also

346

347

348

349

350

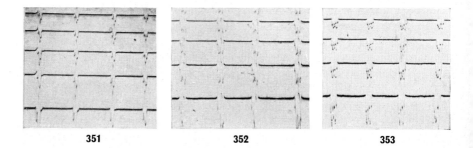

351

352

353

Plates 346-353

established that the initial cuts with the polished edge are far sharper than those with the natural edge. We have thus a guide as to which diamond to select for which specific purpose. If a limited number of very sharp cuts is required, for say cutting graticules or for any other reason, the *polished* diamond should be selected. If *prolonged* wear is involved, and this is what happens in a glazier's industrial tool, a *natural* edge should give better life. A natural edge, if carefully selected, would appear to be advantageous in the making of large line gratings, where the ultimate failure of the diamond is decisive. Against this must be balanced the advantageous very narrow sharpness of the polished stone. But this sharpness will not be long maintained. Hence it is strongly advised that for cutting gratings a search should be made to secure a sharp natural edge, for this will last very much longer. It will be recalled that 100,000 lines on a 15 cm grating represents something like 16 km of cut.

This account is merely an interim report, for the investigations are being actively pursued. One item under examination is the influence of cooling on wear ; it appears to be significant if hydrogen gas is used as coolant.

REFERENCE

Letter Z.

PART EIGHT

APPENDIX
ADDENDUM
BIBLIOGRAPHY
INDEX

APPENDIX

Fringes of Equal Tangential Inclination

A BRIEF description will be given here of a multiple-beam interference system which I have named ' fringes of equal tangential inclination '. First developed in 1950, they have numerous interesting purely optical characteristics which will not, however, be discussed here. Attention is drawn only to this interferometric system because of some possibilities in connection with topographical studies, although these have not as yet been exploited. The fringes are based upon multiple-beam interference produced by a *cylindrically curved thin film* which is suitably silvered on both sides. Much of interferometry requires the employ of planes or near-by planes, and involves relatively small ranges of angles of incidence. The system about to be described is unique in that the whole gamut of angles of incidence from 0° to 90° is exploited, through using a surface bent into a complete semicircle and directing on to it a beam of parallel light along the direction of the axis of bending. The optical system is very simple. A parallel beam of strictly mono-chromatic light is incident on a doubly-silvered piece of mica which is bent convexly into a cylinder. The mica thickness t must be small compared with the radius of curvature R (say 1/1000th part). Although all the beams strike the cylinder parallel to the axial line, it is clear that the angles of incidence vary continuously from 0° to 90° on going up from the axis across the beam. As the two ' parallel ' curved surfaces are silvered, the constant thickness between these leads to the formation of a type of highly localized sharp multiple-beam fringes (see S. Tolansky and N. Barakat, *Proc. Phys. Soc.*, **63B**, 545, 1950).

From the geometry of the system it can be shown that the succes-sively multiple reflected beams all have the same effective retardation. For a radius of curvature of some 2 cm and a film thickness of some 0·002 cm all the multiple-reflected beams effectively meet in a small region approximating to a line. As a result of this the Airy summation condition virtually applies exactly and so one obtains highly sharpened multiple-beam fringes with a good sharpened intensity distribution. A computation of the optical properties of the system shows that the successive orders of interference will appear at distances from the axis corresponding to the appropriate angles of incidence which lead to whole numbers of waves of retardation. Straight-line fringes appear, and it is not too difficult to prove that they are sharply localized in a plane passing through the centre of curvature. If a screen is placed in this plane very sharp fringes appear on it, or alternatively they can be photographed by focussing on this plane.

The fringe system has some interesting optical properties for the fringes viewed in reflection, and furthermore the localization is dependent upon whether the incident beam falls on the concave or the convex face first. Again, both monochromatic fringes, or the corresponding white-light fringes can be produced, by throwing an image of the fringe pattern on to the slit of a spectrograph, for the localization is the same for all wavelengths. The fringe system is particularly easily produced with a thin sheet of doubly silvered mica bent cylindrically by holding it between metal plates in which circular grooves have been cut. Since a good selected mica can exhibit remarkable uniformity of thickness, such a material, when silvered, fulfils the necessary conditions. It is, however, a crystalline material and this affects the fringe pattern, which then depends upon the direction of bending relative to the optical axial plane.

The birefringent properties of the mica lead to a polarization fringe doubling and in order to simplify the pattern in the first instance it is desirable for a polarizer to be introduced. When this is done a fringe pattern is obtained such as that shown in Plate 354 ($\times$ 4). These fringes are very sharp and critically localized on the predicted plane. It can be proved that the radius of the $(p + 1)$th ring for a wavelength λ is effectively $R\sqrt{\dfrac{\mu\lambda}{t}(p - \epsilon)}$ where μ is the refractive index and ϵ the fractional order of interference at the centre of the system. Dispersion is thus proportional to the radius R and inversely as $t^{1/2}$. For a radius R of 5 cm and a thickness t of 1/50th mm, and taking ϵ conveniently as zero (which merely means an integral pattern at the centre), then the radius of the fifth ring is about 4 cm for the green line of mercury. The fringe pattern is therefore easily secured at low magnifications.

If the sheet of mica has cleavage steps on it then the pattern secured reveals these. Plate 355 ($\times$ 4) was obtained with a sheet of mica selected to show the cleavage step effect. *It is clear that we have here an alternative optical method for studying the topographies of thin sheets.* Very high dispersions can simply be obtained by merely increasing R. Notable is the exceptional sharpness of the outer order fringes. The reason is to be found in the fact that these higher order fringes correspond to quite high angles of incidence, possibly 70° or even more. It is

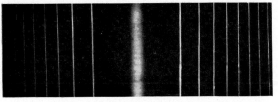

354

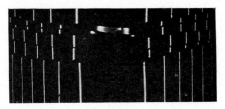

355

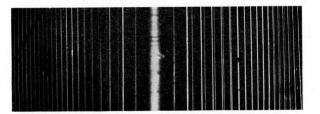

356

357

Plates 354-357

demonstrable both by theory and experiment that the reflectivity of a surface increases with increasing incidence, thus it is that the higher the incidence, the greater is the reflectivity of the silver and the sharper are the fringes.

This arrangement lends itself to high-precision measurement of the thickness of a thin dielectric film deposited on to the mica. By selecting a sheet of mica free from cleavages, the thin film, when put down over half the mica before silvering, will lead to a step exactly as with a cleavage step and so the thin film step height can be secured. A value of the refractive index will have to be assumed and several radiations might be needed to ensure that overlapping of orders can be detected if the film is appreciably thicker than $\lambda/2$. A change of one order in the mica corresponds to a thickness change of 1700 Å (not the usual 2730 Å) because the refractive index of the mica is involved.

There is a marked fall-off in intensity with increasing fringe order, and this is primarily due to an increase in the *absorption* of silver with increasing angle of incidence. On removal of the polarizer the fringe pattern presents some curious properties, and an example of such a pattern is shown in Plate 356 ($\times$ 4). Beginning at the centre and moving out to the left, the fringes first appear in pairs, one sharper than the other. The pairs close up and coalesce, then they open up and the sharper component moves away, becoming rapidly weaker as it sharpens. These properties can be completely accounted for in terms of *two* quite different and unrelated optical properties, the one the *birefringence* of the mica, the other the *differential phase change* on reflection at silver when the incidence is other than normal.

Because of the birefringence, a ray incident on to the mica crystal splits into two rays polarized mutually perpendicularly. The refractive index differs for these two beams so the effective optical thickness of the mica differs for the two, hence each fringe doubles into two polarized components. The ordinary refractive index remains constant but the refractive index of the extraordinary ray is itself a function of the angle of incidence. The outer fringe is that for the light vibrating in the plane of incidence and the separation of the two components vanishes to zero at an angle of incidence equal to the optic axial angle, in which direction both refractive indices are the same. It will be remembered that the fringes correspond to progressive increase in incidence. Beyond this angle the fringes cross over and the separation progressively increases. That the one system of fringes is much sharper than the other is also in accord with optical theory, according to which the one polarization has consistently a higher reflectivity than the other, and it is this polarization which has the sharper fringes, in agreement with expectation.

However, the vanishing of the doublet separation is not quite at the crystallographically expected position, and in any case the rate of move-out of the sharper component from the zero position is too rapid. Furthermore this component becomes anomalously weak. All these secondary difficulties are completely accounted for by the onset of effects due to the differential phase change at reflection at the silver as the incidence increases. This effect which was first reported in 1944 (S. Tolansky, *Phil. Mag.*, **35**, 179, 1944) applies to all multiple-beam systems using silver when the angle of incidence is other than normal. The properties are as follows.

Consider a Fizeau fringe multiple-beam wedge system illuminated with parallel monochromatic light, producing straight parallel fringes. Now let the incidence be increased, the light still remaining parallel. The fringes are seen to broaden and at an incidence of 20° are seen just to become double. As incidence increases, one set of fringes detaches itself and moves outwards to the higher order, becoming progressively sharper and weaker than the companion set. Both sets are found to be plane-polarized mutually perpendicularly. The same effect is true also for fringes of equal chromatic order. Plate 357 ($\times$ 30) illustrates the character of the effect observed at an incidence of 55°. The central pattern shows the fringe doubling, the one set much sharper than the other. Above and below are the two pictures obtained respectively by the insertion of polaroids, set at right angles, proving that the two components are polarized, mutually perpendicularly.

Since these fringes are produced by an *air* film between two silvered glass plates, no question of birefringence is involved. The explanation is in fact simple. In accordance with electromagnetic theory a difference in phase is introduced at non-normal incidence between light vibrating with the electric vector parallel to or perpendicular to the plane of incidence. Thus the interferometric gap appears to be different to the two directions of vibration. The reduction in intensity of the sharper component reveals something new, it shows that there is *differential absorption* as well as differential phase change. This will not be discussed further here.

To return now to Plate 356. It is clear that the curious fringe doubling seen there is in fact a combination of the effect of birefringence and of differential phase change at reflection, and detailed measurement confirms that these two factors together account for the effects observed.

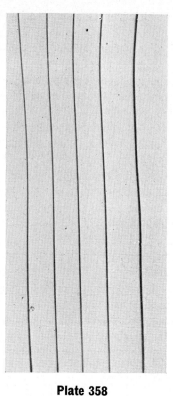

Plate 358

ADDENDUM

In completion of this treatise yet two more fringe photographs will be reproduced. One is shown in Plate 358 with the fairly high magnification of × 300. This plate shows the reflection multiple-beam Fizeau fringe pattern given by *two pieces of fire-polished blown glass*. It is quite evident that such glass is really smooth and completely free from structure. It is such surfaces which have been systematically used as matching surfaces throughout the whole of the work described in this treatise, and Plate 358 shows with what confidence the numerous observed microtopographies can be relied upon.

This treatise will be concluded with an exceptionally fine example of extremely high resolution shown in Plate 359. It reveals microstructure on a synthetic quartz crystal. This fringe pattern is remarkable in that the magnification in extension is microscopically very high (× 1350) whilst magnification in height-depth is actually almost × 1,000,000. A 4 mm apochromatic objective of numerical aperture 0·95 was used.

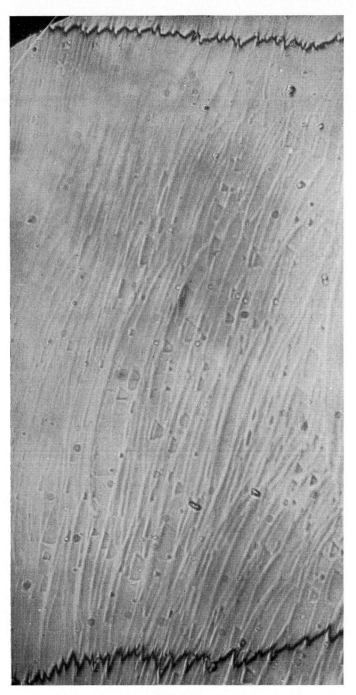

Plate 359

This interferogram was obtained with a thin-film collodion technique. The crystal was first silvered, then on this was poured a dilute solution of collodion in acetone. A thin film from such a dilute solution has close contouring properties on its lower surface but the top layer also tends to follow the bottom, i.e. a ' parallel-sided ' film tends to form. This is not what is required for interferometry, hence, immediately after pouring on the dilute collodion and before it has fully dried, an appreciably thicker solution of collodion is then poured over. This produces a smooth final surface, which is then silvered. Interference takes place in the thin film between the silvered topographical structure and the silvered smooth upper surface.

The refractive index μ of our collodion film is 1·400 so that fringe separation ($\lambda/2\mu$) is less than when in air. With the green mercury line the order separation is 1950 Å. Measured fringe width is about 1/130th of an order, i.e. the fringe occupies only 15 Å. With our resolution criterion of 1/5th of a fringe width, resolution is here 3 Å. The unique resolution is attributable to both the high reflectivity and the very close approach of the two surfaces.

Particular attention is drawn to the close contouring efficiency for each kink can be identified with a surface feature.

REFERENCES

Nos. 21, 29, C.

BIBLIOGRAPHY

This bibliographical list consists of : (*a*) papers published by the author on the subject of multiple-beam interferometry, and (*b*) titles of theses of students who have worked for a higher degree under the immediate direction of the author. References to work by others are given in the text itself as and when they occur. At the end of each chapter a brief list of the appropriate references from this bibliography is given. The scheme of numeration is as follows : papers are numbered 1 to 56 and theses A to Z. Theses A and F are available at the library of Manchester University, all the remainder being at the Library of London University.

Author's Papers on Interferometry

1. TOLANSKY, S. 'New Non-localized Interference Fringes ', *Phil. Mag.*, **34**, 555, 1943.
2. —— 'An Interferometric Procedure for the Examination of Crystal Surfaces ', *Nature*, **152**, 722, 1943.
3. —— ' New Interference Phenomena with Newton's Rings ', *Phil. Mag.*, **35**, 120, 1944.
4. —— ' Topography of a Quartz Crystal Face ', *Nature*, **153**, 195, 1944.
5. —— ' Differential Polarization Phase Change on Reflection ', *Phil. Mag.*, **35**, 179, 1944.
6. —— ' Topography of a (100) Face on Quartz ', *Proc. Roy. Soc.*, **A**, **184**, 41, 1945.
7. —— ' Topography of Cleavage Faces of Mica and Selenite ', *Proc. Roy. Soc.*, **A**, **184**, 51, 1945.
8. —— ' New Multiple-Beam White-Light Fringes ', *Phil. Mag.*, **36**, 225, 1945.
9. —— ' Further Interferometric Studies with Mica ', *Proc. Roy. Soc.*, **A**, **186**, 261, 1946.
10. —— ' Low-Order Multiple-Beam Interferometry ', *Proc. Phys. Soc.*, **58**, 654, 1946.
11. TOLANSKY, S. and WILCOCK, W. L. ' Topography of the Face of a Diamond Crystal ', *Nature*, **157**, 583, 1946.
12. TOLANSKY, S., and KHAMSAVI, A. ' Cleavage of Calcite ', *Nature*, **157**, 661, 1946.
13. TOLANSKY, S. ' Interferometric Studies on Mica ', *Phil. Mag.*, **37**, 390, 1946.
14. —— ' Interferometric Studies on Mica ', *Phil. Mag.*, **37**, 453, 1946.
15. TOLANSKY, S., and KHAMSAVI, A. ' Cleavage of Selenite and Mosaic Structure ', *Nature*, **158**, 519, 1946.

16. T O L A N S K Y, S. 'Intensity Efficiency of the Fabry-Perot Interferometer', *Physica*, **12**, 649, 1946.

17. T O L A N S K Y, S., and F A U S T, A. 'A Transparent Replica Technique for Interferometry', *Proc. Phys. Soc.*, **59**, 951, 1947.

18. T O L A N S K Y, S., and W I L C O C K, W. L. 'Interference Studies on Diamond. Crossed Fringes', *Proc. Roy. Soc.*, **A**, **191**, 182, 1947.

19. T O L A N S K Y, S., and M O R R I S, P. G. 'Interferometric Survey of the Micas', *Min. Mag.*, **28**, 198, 1947.

20. T O L A N S K Y, S., and B A R D S L E Y, W. 'Interferometric Study of Oscillating Quartz Crystals', *Nature*, **161**, 925, 1948.

21. T O L A N S K Y, S., and B A R A K A T, N. 'New Localized Interference Fringes', *Nature*, **162**, 816, 1948.

22. T O L A N S K Y, S. *Multiple-Beam Interferometry*, Clarendon Press, Oxford, 1948.

23. T O L A N S K Y, S., and R A N A D E, J. D. 'Reflection Interferometry for Weak Sources', *R.A.S. Monthly Notices*, **109**, 86, 1949.

24. T O L A N S K Y, S. 'New Application of White-Light Fringes of Superposition', *Nature*, **163**, 637, 1949.

25. T O L A N S K Y, S., and N I C H O L S, D. G. 'Interferometric Examination of Hardness Test Indentations', *Nature*, **164**, 103, 1949.

26. T O L A N S K Y, S., and A U S T I N, E. 'Abrasion Tests on Diamonds', *Nature*, **164**, 193, 1949.

27. T O L A N S K Y, S., and H O L D E N, J. 'Interferometric Study of Slip-Bands on Metal Crystals', *Nature*, **164**, 754, 1949.

28. T O L A N S K Y, S., and N I C H O L S, D. G. 'Interferometric Examination of Hardness Indentations on Tin', *Nature*, **164**, 840, 1949.

29. T O L A N S K Y, S., and B A R A K A T, N. 'New Fringes Formed with Curved Thin Sheets', *Proc. Phys. Soc.*, **B**, **63**, 545, 1950.

30. T O L A N S K Y, S. 'Interferometric Evaluation of the Thickness of Thin Films', *Journ. de Phys. et le Radium*, **11**, 373, 1950.

31. —— 'Application of Interferometry to Electro-deposited Films', *J. Electrodepositors Tech. Soc.*, **27**, 171, 1951.

32. T O L A N S K Y, S., and B A R D S L E Y, W. 'Interferometric Studies on Vibrations of Quartz Crystals', *Proc. Phys. Soc.*, **64B**, 224, 1951.

33. T O L A N S K Y, S. 'Multiple-Beam Interferometry and the Influence of Vacuum Technique', *Vacuum*, **1**, 75, 1951.

34. —— 'Interferometric Studies on Coals', *Nature*, **169**, 660, 1952.

35. T O L A N S K Y, S., and N I C H O L S, D. G. 'Interferometric Studies on Hardness Tests', *Phil. Mag.*, **43**, 410, 1952.

36. T O L A N S K Y, S., and S U L T A N, F. A. 'An Unusual Birefringence Interference Pattern', *Phil. Mag.*, **43**, 547, 1952.

37. T O L A N S K Y, S., and O M A R, M. 'A Thin Film Interference Technique', *Nature*, **170**, 81, 1952.

38. —— —— 'Micro-reference Flat for Multiple-Beam Interferometry', *Journ. Sci. Instr.*, **30**, 337, 1953.

39. T O L A N S K Y , S . , and O M A R , M . ' Observations on Slip in Diamond ', *Phil. Mag.*, **44**, 514, 1953.

40. B E L K , R . , T O L A N S K Y , S . , and T U R N B U L L , A . ' The Use of Multilayer Films in Interferometry ', *J.O.S.A.*, **44**, 5, 1954.

41. T O L A N S K Y , S . , and H O W E S , V . R . ' Optical Studies of Ring Cracks on Glass ', *Proc. Phys. Soc.*, **67B**, 538, 1954.

42. O M A R , M . , P A N D Y A , N . S . , and T O L A N S K Y , S . ' Etching of Diamond Octahedron Faces ', *Proc. Roy. Soc.*, **A**, **225**, 33, 1954.

43. P A N D Y A , N . S . , and T O L A N S K Y , S . ' Etching of Diamond : Cleavage, Dodecahedron and Cube Faces ', *Proc. Roy. Soc.*, **A**, **225**, 40, 1954.

44. H O W E S , V . R . , and T O L A N S K Y , S . ' Pressure Crack Figures on Diamond Octahedral Faces ', *Proc. Roy. Soc.*, **A**, **230**, 287, 1955.

45. T O L A N S K Y , S . , and W I L L I A M S , A . P . ' Directional Hardness Studies on Tin and Bismuth ', *Proc. Phys. Soc.*, **68B**, 548, 1955.

46. T O L A N S K Y , S . ' Rapid Assessment of Multilayers for Interferometry,' *Lab. Practice*, **3**, 361, 1955.

47. —— *Microstructures of Diamond Surfaces*, N.A.G. Press, London, 1955.

48. —— *Introduction to Interferometry*, Longmans Green, London, 1955.

49. E M A R A , S . H . , and T O L A N S K Y , S . ' Precision Multiple-Beam Interference with High Resolution ', *J.O.S.A.*, **45**, 792, 1955.

50. T O L A N S K Y , S . , and B H I D E , V . G . ' Sur La Reproduction des Reliefs par les Couches Minces ', *Journ. de Chim. Phys.*, p. 563, 1956.

51. E M A R A , S . H . , and T O L A N S K Y , S . ' Microstructure of Dodecahedral Faces of Diamond ', *Proc. Roy. Soc.*, **A**, **239**, 289, 1957.

52. T O L A N S K Y , S . , and H O W E S , V . R . ' Induction of Ring Cracks on Diamond Surfaces ', *Proc. Phys. Soc.*, **70B**, 521, 1957.

53. P A T E L , A . R . , and T O L A N S K Y , S . ' Etching of Crystal Cleavages, I, Mica ', *Proc. Roy. Soc.*, **A**, **243**, 35, 1957.

54. —— —— ' Etching of Crystal Cleavages, II, Diamond ', *Proc. Roy. Soc.*, **A**, **243**, 41, 1957.

55. T O L A N S K Y , S . , and W O O D , A . F . B . ' Multiple-Beam Interferometric Studies on Oscillating Quartz Crystals ', *Physica*, **24**, 508, 1958.

56. T O L A N S K Y , S . ' Modulated Multiple-Beam Interference Fringes ', *Lab. Practice*, **5**, 457, 1958.

Degree Theses from the Author's Laboratory

A. P. G. Morris, M.Sc. Manchester 1946, ' Electrical Properties and Structures of Micas '.

B. D. G. Avery, Ph.D. London 1950, ' Some Optical Properties of Thin Films of Silver and other Metals '.

C. N. Barakat, Ph.D. London 1951, ' Interference Studies on Curved Thin Films '.

D. J. Holden, Ph.D. London 1951, ' Interference Studies of Metal Surfaces '.

E. W. Bardsley, Ph.D. London 1951, ' Interferometric Studies on Quartz Crystals '.

F. W. L. Wilcock, Ph.D. Manchester 1951, ' Studies of the Topography of Diamond Surfaces '.

G. E. M. Wilks, Ph.D. London 1952, ' Interferometric Studies on Natural and Polished Diamonds '.

H. B. T. M. Willis, Ph.D. London 1952, ' Interferometric Studies on Growth Features of Quartz Crystals '.

I. F. S. A. Sultan, Ph.D. London 1953, ' Optical and Interferometric Studies on Crystal Growth from Solution '.

J. A. P. Williams, Ph.D. London 1953, ' Interferometric Studies on the Directional Hardness of Some Single Crystals '.

K. M. Omar, Ph.D. London 1953, ' Optical Studies of Growth and Etch on Some Crystal Faces '.

L. J. George, Ph.D. London 1953, ' Optical Studies on Some Metal Alloys '.

M. A. L. Batchelor, Ph.D. London 1954, ' Optical Examination of Spark Erosion Pits '.

N. J. A. Belk, Ph.D. London 1954, ' Optical Studies of Distortion of Metal Surfaces Produced by Indenting '.

O. N. S. Pandya, Ph.D. London 1954, ' Optical Studies on Some Crystal Surfaces, Cleavage and Etch '.

P. V. R. Howes, Ph.D. London 1955, ' Optical Studies of Some Impact Phenomena and Surface Hardness Measurements '.

Q. S. H. Emara, Ph.D. London 1955, ' Optical Studies of Growth Features on the Surfaces of Some Diamonds '.

R. A. F. B. Wood, Ph.D. London 1955, ' Optical Studies on Longitudinal Vibrations in Circular Z-cut Discs '.

S. V. Ramanathan, Ph.D. London 1956, ' Hardness and Surface Studies on Electrodeposited Alloys '.

T. V. G. Bhide, Ph.D. London 1956, ' Interferometric Studies on Some Aspects of Crystal Growth '.

U. R. S. Sharma, Ph.D. London 1956, ' Optical Studies on the Etching of Glasses '.

V. J. B. Ramage, Ph.D. London 1956, ' Optical Studies on Diamond Cleavage Surfaces '.

W. P. M. Reynolds, Ph.D. London 1956, ' Optical Studies of Growth from Solution '.

X. T. Turbadar, Ph.D. London 1957, ' Optical Studies on Metals Subject to Ultrasonic Impact '.

Y. T. R. Barnett, Ph.D. London 1957, ' Optical Studies on Plastic and Metal Surfaces Subjected to High-speed Impact '.

Z. A. R. Patel, Ph.D. London 1957, ' Studies on Cleavage, Fracture and Etching of Diamond '.

INDEX